sINCONVENIENT leep

WHY TEAMS WIN AND LOSE

Pat Byrne & Suzanne Byrne

Book cover design by Luke Culicerto

Book interior design by Andy Meaden meadencreative.com

ISBN: 978-1-7772617-1-9

Dedication

To James Cameron McBride (February 4th, 1974 – June 28th, 1996), our godson, nephew and cousin – our inspiration and motivation. To Stephen Whitfield Smith (April 12th, 1956 – July 19th, 2014), our friend who loved his family and sports and had one speed – full throttle.

Thank you both for keeping our priorities in line and for enriching our lives.

We also want to thank Steven Wright for making us laugh at life. Is there anything better?

Acknowledgements

We would like to thank the many people who have helped us complete this book by generously sharing their time, thoughts, and experiences with us. Specifically, the contributions from the following people are greatly appreciated: Kendal Yonomoto, Cheri Mah, Mike Winters, Dennis LaRue, Vern Gambetta, Liam Mannix, Daniel Kripke, Dion Von Molke, Bill Sweetenham, Brian Underhill, Donna Underhill, and Linda Carole Guy.

We would also like to thank Dr. Z for taking the time to write an exceptionally kind foreword and especially thank him for the many helpful discussions we've had with him over the last decade.

Finally, we thank our loving family, Donna Mae and Julia, for their understanding and patience over the past few years while we obsessed over this book and left hundreds of reference papers and drafts scattered in the dining room which we hastily cleaned up every time we had guests over for dinner.

Contents

Foreword

Leonard Zaichkowsky, Ph.D.

Leonard Zaichkowsky, a professor, researcher, and consultant for almost four decades at Boston University, pioneered sport psychology by bringing cognitive neuroscience and sports performance together as an interdisciplinary science. This farm boy from northern Alberta has made an impact on the world of sport from youth to the professional ranks. Doc Z as he is affectionately known has published four textbooks and a recent best seller, "The Playmakers Advantage" that demonstrates the importance of the brain in sport performance. He has also published over 100 papers in peer reviewed journals, delivered hundreds of presentations world-wide, serves on several journal review boards, is a science advisor for several sport technology companies, and is a co-founder of GameSenseSports, a sport technology company. Len has consulted with teams in the NHL, NFL, NBA, MLB, Sydney Swans (Australian Rules Football), and numerous Olympic Training facilities around the world. Recently the American Psychological Association honored Len with the "Distinguished Service to the Profession" award.

I am pleased and honored to have this opportunity to write the Foreword for the book, *"Inconvenient Sleep: Why Teams Win and Lose"*, authored by Pat and Suzanne Byrne. Our professional relationship began when I arrived in Vancouver to consult with the NHL Canucks in 2009, then came on full time in 2010 as their first director of sport science. Pat, as a Vancouver resident and Canucks fan had already convinced the new progressive Canucks management that they really needed a sleep monitoring and education program to better deal with their extraordinary travel schedule, jet lag, and overall athlete recovery. Although I had broad expertise as a sport scientist, my understanding of sleep, fatigue, and performance was woefully inadequate. But Pat would frequently visit my office and share with me his expertise in sleep science. Suzanne who at the time was attending Queens College in New York City as a student-athlete would often accompany Pat so I also got to know her. Suzanne later went on to Law School at Tulane University studying Sports Law, and now partners with her father in educating organizations about the importance of sleep in high performance sport. Pat and Suzanne provide unparalleled expertise on sleep and performance in this book.

But "Inconvenient Sleep", is not only about educating coaches, sport scientists, and athletes about the relationship between sleep and peak performance, there are also wonderful "gems" in chapters that discuss related issues relevant to sport scientists and followers of sport. For instance, unless the reader is a high performance coach, official, or an athlete that competed at a high level, most would not understand the incredible grind, athletes need to go through to be the best they can be. As a teenager or young adult, athletes tend to drain their mind-body fuel tanks, do not understand the importance of recovery, and truly see sleep just as the authors say in their title, an "inconvenient" necessity. Pat and Suzanne use this opportunity to also educate the readers about the world of research and science, a topic few readers would have encountered in their educational experiences. Clever words are used as Chapter headings to depict movement into the world of science, words such as "Science-ish" and" Research-ish". Wonderful historical stories are shared with the reader, often challenging the reader to be skeptical of statements such as "proven by science". But, is it good science? As such, the reader is made more familiar with what goes into being a good scientist, what is peer reviewed research, why even peer reviewed research can be flawed, and why sleep research, as the authors maintain, "came late to the science party".

For you history buffs, you will enjoy the journey Pat and Suzanne take you through as they describe polygraph (lie detection) research by John Larson, the brain research (EEG) of Hans Berger, through to the early fascinating research on "REM" sleep conducted by Professors Kleitman and Aserinsky, through to modern day interest in conducting research on sleep with athletes. Strength coaches have entered the field of strength and conditioning, likely unaware of its early history. The authors accurately describe the early (1970's), seminal work done at the University of Nebraska that prompted a national and perhaps international movement in the science and practice of functional strength training. At that time myths existed about weight training that were quickly dispelled. Pat and Suzanne believe a similar misunderstanding of sleep and performance is quickly being transformed.

Looking back at Pat's trail blazing consulting with the NHL Vancouver Canucks over a decade ago, who would have thought "sleep science" would have such a dramatic impact on sporting organizations world-wide. As I travel around the world visiting college athletic departments, professional sports teams, and Olympic organizations in Australia, New Zealand, Asia, Europe, South America, and North America, I see Pat Byrne's sleep science fingerprints everywhere. Nearly all sporting organizations are putting a premium on educating their athletes about sleep. This did not exist at the turn of this century. Globally, university faculty as well as graduate students are conducting research, publishing results on important findings, and presenting papers on topics still new to sleep science. But important work still needs to be done. Research grade and consumer grade sleep monitoring devices need to be improved upon, and validated. Can we quantify the benefits of game day napping? How much nap time is needed? When teams travel across time zones do we really know how to make accurate sleep adjustments? Most importantly, how do sleep disorders relate to an athlete's mental health? How do sporting organizations optimally change the sleep behavior of their athletes since we know education alone does not change behavior? Pat and Suzanne write in Chapter 4 that athletes and sports teams need to educate themselves about the evolving field of sleep and performance and they conclude the book with saying, "this is a process". Indeed it is!

CHAPTER 1

Game On

There are many reasons athletes and teams win and lose games. Sleep and jet lag from travel are part of that equation. While professional athletes often travel in comfort, they can still suffer from sleep loss. We explore the inherent factors affecting athletes and go further to show how game officials, college golf and football players, and even race car drivers are also affected by poor sleep and historical scheduling.

There's an old saying that victory has 100 fathers and defeat is an orphan.

President John F. Kennedy

Sports have always been about winning. That is why we have finish lines, why trophies are awarded, it is why we keep score. Winning has been, and still is, about pride. What has changed and evolved over the years are the stakes. Professional sports are big business. Really big business. Two years ago, in 2018, the global sports market was worth 488 billion dollars. That included the top-grossing sports of football, basketball and baseball in the United States (U.S.) and football (soccer) in Europe. For owners of professional sports teams, it is not just about gross revenues, but the valuation of the team. For example, in 2010 the Golden State Warriors were valued at 360 million dollars. Seven years and two championship wins later, in 2017, their valuation was estimated to be 2.6 billion dollars. Winning a couple of championships certainly helps.

The valuation of teams is based on many factors including the sport, the size of the market, the history of the organization, fan loyalty, etc. However, one of the major factors, if not the most important factor, is winning. Fans follow winners. Fans pay money to be associated with winners. It is an emotional attachment.

Successful college teams (i.e. winning teams) can enhance an entire institution. Beyond the revenue, successful athletic programs enhance freshman enrollment, increase institutional donations, improve campus culture and student engagement, and increase student retention and community support. Some

American football coaches are paid in the millions and are often the highest-paid public employee in their state; a huge incentive for them to do everything they can to help their team win (and keep their job). Some coaches make, in excess of, 9 million dollars annually. In 2017, *The Wall Street Journal* published its "College Football Value Rankings". Its top-valued team was the Ohio State Buckeyes worth an eye-popping 1.5 billion dollars. That is college football!

What Is a Sport Anyway?

Of course, sports can mean different things to different people. There are organized professional sports, Olympic sports, college and high school sports, community sports, sports with friends, etc. In 2018, Leigh Steinberg, writing in *Forbes*, addressed the question: what activities legitimately constitute a "sport"?

He noted that there is no real definition of sport. Any dictionary definition leaves out some sports. For example, the "Oxford Dictionary defines sport as 'an activity involving physical exertion and skill in which an individual or a team competes against another or others for entertainment.'"

Steinberg questioned how E-Sports could qualify as a sport. Sure, there are competitions, and sure, millions of people watch and are entertained, but physical exertion? Under the Oxford definition E-Sports would not likely qualify as a sport. Try telling that to the millions of fans that watch E-Sports. Or how about playing a game of cornhole with some friends, a game where you have to throw a beanbag into a hole some distance away. Is that a sport or a game?

In the end Steinberg concluded, "What qualifies as a true sport may be the grist for endless arguments, and the only certainty may be in the eye of the beholder." Any activity is a sport because you say it is. We are all athletes, to some extent.

The "Official" Reason

So, why do teams win and lose games? Talent, skill, coaching, game strategy, equipment, and even luck all play a huge role. Athletes must also be in shape and ready to perform at their best during a game. That includes mental preparation, nutrition, hydration, conditioning and even sleep. There is also one thing that many fans, athletes, and teams feel can affect the outcome of games. That is the officiating. Officials are a critical part of every sport, with the exception of ultimate. There are both professional and amateur officials. According to FIFA, in their 2006 "Big Count" there were about 840,000 soccer referees globally, supervising 265 million soccer players.

Because officials can be a factor in who might win or lose a game, they are often accused of favouritism. There are a number of academic research papers that have looked into referee bias, particularly in European football (soccer). One article published in the 2016 *Journal of Economic Surveys* states that "studies have shown that referees favor the home team."

Such accusations are not restricted to soccer. Also in 2016, Canadian researchers published a paper in the Journal, *Statistical Analysis and Data Mining* entitled, "Biased Penalty Calls in the National Hockey League". The researchers claim that there is indeed bias in the calling of penalties. They argue their statistical analysis shows that more penalties are called on road teams and on the perceived weaker team than on home teams and the perceived stronger teams. In addition, the researchers say that the team with more goals in a game is more likely to get the next penalty. Finally, the study states that if a team accumulates more penalties than their opponent then there will likely be, what is often called in hockey, a "make-up" call, to balance out the infractions.

Of course, leagues in all sports bristle at the notion that officiating is biased at all. Certainly there has been much more done in the past decade to ensure fair calls. There is better training and better supervision of officials in most leagues. There are video reviews and slow-motion reviews from many different angles that can be reviewed to get the call right. However, these steps often take time and slow the game down making it difficult to watch, so each league has their own rules about what can be reviewed and when. The thread that seems to cut across officiating in all sports is that officials can and do make mistakes, regardless of the cause.

One recent example of an unreviewable mistake affecting a game is the 2019 National Football League (NFL) Conference Championship game between the New Orleans Saints and the Los Angeles Rams. The teams were tied late in the game. All the Saints needed was a field goal to win. They wanted to get closer to the goal line and threw a pass to get there. The defender interfered with the receiver and the ball was not caught. That is normally a penalty, and would have moved the Saints closer to the end zone. Had it been called, the Saints would have had the ability to kick an easy field goal and more importantly, the opportunity to run out the clock for the win. The referee didn't call the infraction. The Saints ended up losing the game in overtime and the opportunity to play in the Super Bowl. The play was not one that was reviewable under the NFL rules. It is not clear why the referee made the mistake, but the consequences were enormous.

One thing that is almost never mentioned in any of the literature, whether it be studies or news articles, is sleep and its effects on the decision-making of game officials. It is simply assumed that officials show up at every game and make perfect calls every time. Officials are expected to be good athletes as they are usually on the ice, field, floor, or pitch for the entire game. The reality is that referees are only human and can have good days and bad days. Bad days can be caused by poor sleep. Poor sleep negatively affects reaction time and the ability to concentrate. You make bad decisions when you are tired. Simply put, nothing good happens from poor sleep. Matthew Walker, a professor of neuroscience and psychology at the University of California, Berkeley, put it succinctly:

> Based on ... about 10,000 empirical scientific studies, the number of people who can survive on six of hours of sleep or less without showing any impairment, rounded to a whole number ... is zero.

The very first research paper to examine the sleep of sports officials and its effect on decision-making during a competitive season was published in February 2020. Grace Vincent at Central Queensland University in Australia and her colleagues had 371 officials from 9 different sports in Australia complete an online questionnaire about their sleep and their perceived decision-making.

The researchers said that overall, the officials self-reported lower sleep hours than the sleep recommended for the general population (7 – 9 hours). Interestingly, officials reported sleeping less after night games vs after day games. However, where officials reported low sleep hours before a competition, their self-perceived decision-making was only negatively impacted to a small degree.

The researchers were careful to explain the downfalls of such subjective analysis, but still, this was the first attempt at studying the sleep and decision-making of officials. The research team will be continuing their research using objective measures of sleep.

When a professional athlete on a team is not performing well, the coach can often make a substitute or bench the player. However, there is no such option for referees. If one of them is having a bad day, he or she is there for the entire game, there are no substitutes. Due to travel and scheduling issues, professional athletes often struggle with getting enough good sleep, it is even harder for officials. While officials are often held to the same or higher standards as professional athletes they are not always given the same sleep opportunities or travel luxuries as them.

You're a Bum

In 1973, *The New York Times* printed a headline that read, "Now It's All Right to Call an Umpire a Bum". The state Supreme Court had determined that it's perfectly okay to call an umpire a bum. The case involved two umpires who sued the President of the American League for saying publicly that they were incompetent. The umpires lost because the court found they were "public figures" and therefore allowed to be subjected to such ridicule, as long as there is no malice involved.

It's not easy to get to the point in an umpire's career where people can legally call you a bum. Mike Winters, for example, had to put in many years of hard work to become a Major League umpire and crew chief. He has been called much worse and has gotten into at least one heated discussion with an unhappy player. Such is the life of a Major League umpire.

Mike Winters was born in 1958 in Oceanside, California. As a kid he played Little League Baseball which sparked his desire to become an umpire. He attended San Diego State University, but his heart was in baseball. So, he enrolled in the 5 – 6-week intensive umpire school and went off to work in the minors. He bounced around the various leagues from the Northwest to California then Texas and finally to the Pacific Coast learning the ropes. It was exhausting. When games ended, often after 10 pm, he had to drive to the next game, sometimes 9 – 10 hours away. It was not easy getting sleep or staying in shape, let alone dealing with the fan and league critics and the long hours of boredom behind the wheel. Winters has said that all minor league umpires have one thing in common: "Everyone wants out."

Winters made his Major League Baseball (MLB) debut in 1988 and is now a crew chief. That means flying first class, staying in nice hotels and eating in nice restaurants. But the days can be long and getting good sleep and staying in shape is still a challenge. The umpires are on the road for 6 months at a time and receive 4 weeks of vacation during the season. They work about 127 games in a season and fly 25,000 – 30,000 miles each year.

Creating schedules for the umpires is tricky because umpires are not supposed to work a game with the same teams within

18 days. The umpires are also supposed to receive similar scheduling benefits to the teams for rest. When teams travel from west to east they get a day off and are required to take a day off after 20 straight days of playing. The umpires are supposed to get a day off when they travel from the West Coast to the East Coast (crossing 3 time zones), although it doesn't always work that way. Winters has worked as many as 45 straight days without a break.

Then there are make-up games or rainout games, double headers and overtime, extending the umpires' days. In 2015, Winters was umpiring a game at Yankee Stadium that went 19 innings and lasted 6 and a half hours. Umpire fatigue is real. Recognizing this, the league has tried to provide the umpires with some guidance. Winters jokingly recalled a time the league tried to offer the umpires guidance on sleep:

> … MLB had a sleep specialist come and address the umpires a few years ago. He told us how important sleep was. (Duh). And how beneficial and restorative it is. (Again, Duh.) He spoke for over an hour. At the end, my only question was, "OK we get how important it is. Now tell us how to make it happen without 27 Miller Lites."

Winters uses humour to point out a real problem that plagues athletes and officials. Athletes and officials often have a hard time getting to sleep after games. For nighttime games that end at 10 pm it is not unusual to be awake until 1 or 2 in the morning and even later. It is just hard to relax and get into the mood to sleep after a game.

Staying in shape and getting proper sleep is just as important for umpires. They have to be agile and be able to move into the right position and at the right time to see and judge a call. Gone are the old days of the overweight, slow umpires. The old joke was an umpire would go into a restaurant and order a large pizza for himself:

> Waiter: "Sir would you like that pizza cut in 4 pieces or 8 pieces?"
>
> Umpire: "Better cut it in 4, I can't eat 8."

That clearly isn't relevant anymore as everyone has the same health expectations for umpires as they do for the players. However, umpires don't have trainers on the road with them and sometimes not even adequate facilities to keep in shape. In addition, working consecutive night games with extensive travel almost ensures the umpires don't get the sleep they need to perform at their best.

Ice Hockey

Dennis LaRue, now a retired NHL referee, worked 1,222 games in the NHL, "the most by an[y] American referee." He was born in Savannah, Georgia in 1959, not quite a hotbed of ice hockey. His family was in the military and moved around to various cities eventually landing in Spokane, Washington. There LaRue played hockey and took up refereeing to make extra money. Like many in his profession, he started refereeing in the minor leagues in Canada, eventually moving to the American Hockey League and then onto the NHL in 1991. In the early days he flew as many as 150,000 miles a year. As the league and the rules evolved those number decreased, but the travel by planes, trains and automobiles still remained quite grueling. LaRue would often be on the road for 7 – 10 days before going home for a break. It would often take him 11 hours of travel in a day to get home, just to have one day off with his family.

The referees travel on commercial airlines and often internationally, having to go through customs checks. With long road trips, the referees usually have bags to check which need to be retrieved at the end of the flight. Of course, sometimes luggage gets lost. They have a solution: each team keeps extra referee uniforms and skates available at the arenas for such emergencies.

The NHL plays most of its games at night, usually ending around 10 pm. Referees have to find a way back to their hotel to eat, although some teams provide post-game meals to the officiating staff. Then it's off to sleep late at night. Getting to sleep before 1 am is a luxury. But early morning flights out the next day are standard. LaRue said he noticed, over the years, that when he and his fellow referees did not sleep well it led to illness and injury.

Basketball

The National Basketball Association (NBA) is not much different than the NHL. Both play an 82-game schedule, 41 games at home and 41 games on the road. Both play mostly evening games and a certain number of games on consecutive nights, called back-to-back games. Both leagues have a similar number of teams spread across North America. In fact, it has been reported that it was some of the original 6 NHL team owners that started the NBA. Like all arena owners, they wanted it to be used as much as possible. The NBA teams could play in the NHL arenas while the hockey teams were on the road. Even today, many of the NBA teams will play out of the same arenas as the city's NHL team. Their seasons are also quite similar as they both start and stop within a few weeks of each other. NBA referees have similar issues to NHL referees in terms of travel and sleep, but their work takes them a bit closer to the fans. An ESPN article described how they have to do their job:

> ... while enraged fans spew venom about your mother, your face, your body, your sexuality, your profession. Coaches will bait you, players will defy you. Nobody is on your side except your fellow officials. It is a virtual guarantee that in the waning minutes of a tight game, you will make a call that will delight 50 percent of the crowd and incense the other 50 percent. And, seconds later, it's entirely possible the roles of those rabid fan bases will be reversed, leading the entire arena on a roller-coaster ride of heated emotions.

Marc Davis, has been an NBA referee for over 22 years, officiating 1,279 regular season games. Davis spoke to *Men's Journal* about how he keeps in shape for running four or five miles a night up and down the court, to try to keep up with some of the best athletes in the world. In addition, he discussed the challenges of sleep:

> The days can morph into each other. ... We can be up until 3 a.m., finishing the game from the night before, then be on the first flight in the morning to the next city. It's a physically demanding job – travelling between time zones, different hotel rooms, and still having to perform that evening. Nobody really cares about how much sleep

you got that night – you still need to call the game.

Scientific research into how poor sleep affects the decision-making and health of officials is in its infancy, but there is plenty of evidence that poor sleep affects athletic performance generally and anecdotal evidence that officials are not an exception.

Participation in a Sport has Benefits

While winning is often the goal of playing sports, there are many reasons people engage in sports including improving mental and physical health, the enjoyment of the game, the comradery, and the competition. Another is to get a free university education. Attending university, particularly in the United States, can be expensive, often ranging from about $80,000 to over $200,000 for a four-year degree, including tuition and living expenses. Some students have the opportunity to both attend university for free and play their favourite sport.

The National Collegiate Athletic Association (NCAA) is an organization based in Indianapolis, Indiana that regulates many student-athletes in the United States and Canada. Its website sums up its scope:

> Nearly half a million college athletes make up the 19,886 teams that send more than 57,661 participants to compete each year in the NCAA's 90 championships in 24 sports across 3 divisions.

In 1910, the Intercollegiate Athletic Association was renamed the NCAA. As early as 1973, the NCAA was divided into three levels: Division I, Division II and Division III. The first two divisions are permitted to provide athletic scholarships while Division III schools are not.

The NCAA is funded largely by marketing and television rights and its Division I Men's Basketball Tournament, which by itself, accounts for about one billion dollars, or about 75% of its annual revenue. It's called March Madness for a reason.

While the universities, colleges, and NCAA support many student-athletes with free tuition and other expenses it is not easy to get a spot on an NCAA team. Take men's football for example. The NCAA estimates that there are about 1,006,012 high school boys' football players in the U.S. Of those players, about 7.3% or 73,712 will end up as NCAA student-athletes playing football. Further, only about 1.6% of those athletes (254) will go on to play in the NFL. In total, about 0.025% of high school football players in the U.S. will end up playing in the NFL. Even those that end up playing in the National Football League only have an average career of 2.6 years.

The NCAA recognizes that academics are an integral part of its program and it therefore provides "state-of-the-art technology, tutoring and access to academic advisers." It says that in its Division I programs nearly 90% of the student-athletes receive a degree. The NCAA also restricts the amount of time athletes can spend playing sports. After all, student-athletes also have academic responsibilities and social and family commitments.

To that end, the NCAA created what is known as Countable Athletically Related Activities (CARA) hours. They limit student-athletes' athletic activities to four hours a day and 20 hours a week during the season. This is supposed to leave the students plenty of time for academics and other commitments (including sleep). Except, in practice, it doesn't actually work that way.

There are many exceptions to the rule, meaning it is not unusual for student-athletes to spend 40–50 hours a week on athletics. These exceptions can include medical check-ins, required team meals, and mandatory travel time to and from games. One large exception is anything the players do voluntarily. There is of course no such thing as "voluntary" anything in college football … or any college sport. If you don't attend a voluntary practice you likely just volunteered yourself to sit on the bench. However, student-athletes are always trying to improve their skills and prove themselves in college sports, so they generally try to practice as much as possible. But, there are only so many hours in a week, so spending extra time on athletics means spending less time on academics, social and family commitments, and often sleep.

You Just Won a Football Scholarship, Welcome to Your New Life.

In Division I football, the season typically starts with a month-long grueling training camp. The players are up before 6:30 am and begin with breakfast, meetings and film, and walk-through plays. Then they have lunch, injury treatment, more meetings, full practice, team dinner, and even more meetings. Lights are generally out at 10:30 pm, and the players try to get to sleep because they are up early the next morning to start again.

Some teams have full-padded practices twice a week. On these days the teams often give players a 3-hour break in the middle of the day. It's a chance to rest and possibly take a nap, although that is hard to do. The players have three hours to themselves and during that time they have to return to where they're staying (often a hotel), have lunch, talk to family and friends and return back to the facility. Since this is the only time during the day they have for themselves, many players also catch up on social media and watch television. Sleeping is low on the priority list for even the most dedicated players. Also, after having an intense practice in the morning it is not easy to fall asleep quickly for a nap. The good news is; this is only until school starts – then the real work begins.

At Northwestern University when classes begin the days get busier. This is what the football team's schedule has looked like in the past:

On Mondays all injured players report to the training room for treatment at 6:15 am. Then the team has meetings and weightlifting. Then players go to classes. On Tuesdays, Wednesdays and Thursdays they have the same routine except they have full-gear practices and positional meetings from 7:50 am until 11:50 am.

By then their CARA hours are up. However, drills are often held and monitored by an athletic trainer or captains as coaches cannot participate past the players' CARA hours. Players that don't participate are often in their coach's office reviewing film for a few hours. On Fridays, if they have a home game, they meet at 3 pm for meetings and to watch film, have a team dinner, then lights are out at 10:30 pm.

If the team has an away game its Friday schedule is different. For example, in a game on November 9, 2012, against the University of Michigan their schedule was:

8:20 Breakfast

8:45 Walk-through

10:00 – 16:30 Bus ride to Michigan

16:30 – 18:00 Stadium walk-through and position meetings

18:00 – 22:30 Team dinner then optional chapel and a movie

22:30 Lights out

Saturday is game day. There is a 7:30 am wake-up call as breakfast starts at 8:05 am. They have a team meeting and then at 8:45 am the bus leaves for the stadium. Once they reach the stadium, they receive treatment for any injuries and warm up until the game starts at noon. Most games last about three hours, but this game went into overtime and took four hours to complete. After the game ended the players received treatment for injuries, got showered and changed, were made available to the media, and were back on the bus for another five-hour ride back to campus. They arrived back at about 10 pm and had Sunday off.

Sometimes teams travel by plane to get to their opponent's stadium. Some teams, like the Iowa University Hawkeyes, charter flights so there are no delays. However, charter flights don't always prevent sleep deprivation from a late game. For instance, one time the Hawkeyes played a 7 pm game in Arizona which ended at 11 pm Eastern Time. Although the team left right after the game, they didn't land back in Iowa until 3:30 am. From the airport the team needed to get on a bus that took them back to school and for those that didn't live in the dorms, they had to get in their cars and drive home. This means the players didn't get home until closer to 5 am Sunday morning. The next day, the players had to do homework, lift weights and watch film. Such sleep loss is not made up easily. It takes a week of good sleep to make-up that kind of sleep loss.

The players also have to maintain their body weights every

week. This often involves late-night feasting with trips to fast food joints or chugging a gallon of milk – whatever it takes to make the weight variance assigned by the strength staff. It all takes time and eating large meals close to bedtime can make sleep difficult, adding to their woes.

Think about what it would be like to work 40 – 50 hours a week and then go to university full-time and try to have a social life. Something has to give, and it is usually sleep.

Golf

Golf is one of the 24 sports played in the NCAA, but not one most people immediately think has travel or sleep issues. At Seattle University, the team is coached by Marc Chandonnet who sets the team schedules, but much of it is dictated by necessity and geography. The team plays weekend tournaments often having to leave by 5 am on a Friday to catch a flight to their destination. Once they land, they rent a car and head straight to the golf course, grabbing food along the way. There they play a round, chart the course, and get in some practice. Then it is off to the hotel to have dinner and try to get to bed by 9 or 10 pm.

Saturday morning is the start of a two-day tournament. The team is up by 5 am. They have the continental breakfast at the hotel, although they have to fight the other teams staying at the same hotel for what is often left of the "complimentary" breakfast. It seems the competition actually starts at breakfast!

They normally arrive at the golf course around 6:15 am for warmup and preparation for the 7:30 am shotgun start (where there are players starting on every hole at once). They play two full rounds of golf (36 holes). That takes about 11 hours of intense competition, then the team goes out for dinner and heads back to the hotel for some sleep.

Sunday morning starts at 5 am again. They play 18 holes, attend an award ceremony, and by 4 pm they are at the airport waiting for their flight home. Depending how far they have to travel, they are often back in Seattle by 7 pm and home by 9 pm to try to cram in some homework and sleep before class the next morning.

The Oregon State golf team has a similarly busy schedule. Here's one example of what it is like to play back-to-back tournaments:

Saturday:

Up at 6:00, travel to Tacoma, play 18-hole practice round, bed by 23:30.

Sunday:

Up at 9:00, play 18 holes, in bed at 22:00.

Monday:

Up at 5:30, play 36 holes of golf, in bed by 22:00.

Tuesday:

Up at 5:30, play 18 holes of golf, drive to Portland, in bed by 22:00.

Wednesday:

Up at 3:50 for a flight to Columbus, Ohio, in bed by 22:00.

Thursday:

Up at 9:00, golf practice, afternoon watching the Masters Golf Tournament on television, bed by 22:30.

Friday:

Up at 7:30, 18-hole practice round, in bed by 22:30.

Saturday:

Up at 5:30, play 36 holes of golf, dinner at 20:00, in bed at 22:30.

Sunday:

Up at 6:10, play 18 holes of golf, back to the airport, flight delays, arrive home at 2 in the morning and in bed by 2:30.

Monday:

Classes.

The NCAA acknowledges that there are problems. It formed the "Inter-association Task Force on Sleep and Wellness", that reviewed the issue and made recommendations for athletes and teams.

The Inter-association said that poor sleep can affect student athletic and academic performance and increase injury risk and recovery as well as the risk of increasing mental health symptoms and disorders. It also said that, on average during their seasons, student-athletes are getting about 6.27 hours of sleep instead of 8 hours each night, and that 61% of student-athletes report daytime fatigue.

They recommended that student-athletes maintain a regular sleep schedule, seek bright light in the daytime, keep their bedroom cool, avoid caffeine and alcohol and excessive food, avoid clock watching, avoid naps and use their beds only for sleep and not for watching television or reading.

The NCAA recommends that universities "consider" learning more about the time demands of student-athletes by conducting a survey, sleep screen the athletes for sleep disorders, and provide sleep education to athletes and coaches.

Car Racing

Not all young athletes find their sport at university. Dion Von Molke is a race car driver who drives an Audi R8 LMS in the Rolex Sports Car Series and a Porsche 911 GT3 in the American Le Mans Series. He enters twelve to thirteen competitions a year that each last from 2 – 24 hours. In 2013, at the age of 23, Von Molke won the 24 hours of Daytona. That race involves 4 drivers switching off every few hours and trying to eat and get some sleep in-between driving at the noisy track. The team manger coordinates the racers and assists the drivers with information, staying awake for the 24-hour race. He is usually awake for closer to 32 hours by the time it is over. (In New Jersey it is a criminal offense to be awake 24 hours and drive on public roads because being awake that long means you have the reaction time and ability to concentrate equivalent to someone who is legally drunk).

Von Molke loves his work, stating, "one of the fascinating parts about our side of racing in endurance is that when you have different categories of cars racing there are four different races going on at once". Different categories of cars go different speeds and are all on the track at the same time. "As a driver at night all you see is lights and you have to be able to distinguish which ones are in your class, which ones aren't, what are the closing speeds, who are you battling with, what cars you're racing and who the driver is and negotiate the traffic and as well as be able to drive your own race." Fortunately, he gets help from the team manager - the one who stays awake for the entire 24-hour race.

Von Molke has to be in top physical condition as well as being at his peak mentally. He knows that at speeds of 185 – 190 miles per hour, in a blink of an eye he could go from being in the lead to being a pile of metal and fiberglass on the side of the course. And it is not just him and the manager. The pit crew has to stay awake for the full 24 hours and refuel and replace the tires every 50 minutes. There is no time for sleep and no time to make mistakes.

Von Molke works on his mental game with a neurotracker and spends 2 – 3 hours in the gym every day to stay in shape. To stay at the top of his game Von Molke knows that sleep is important. "I notice in myself that if I take a red eye or don't get the sleep I need, it hurts me mentally and I can tell sleep plays a big part in my performance."

Car racing, like many sports can have systemic issues concerning scheduling that make it impossible for athletes to get the sleep they need. If you have a 24-hour race, you are not sleeping. The same is true for many sports that involve travel, early mornings and late nights. No amount of sleep education can remove the built-in problems. Those take a lot more effort and creativity.

Sports Leagues

Sports leagues determine their own playing schedule for the season. However, the leagues often negotiate travel and days off terms with the players in their collective bargaining agreements. All of the major North American sports leagues have undergone expansions in the past few decades. They have more teams, play more games, and travel more often than they ever have. The number of games each team or league plays and when they play them has largely been dictated by history, economics, the availability of arenas, broadcasting or TV rights, and geography. As sleep science has progressed, sports leagues, teams, and athletes have begun to understand that travel and changes in circadian rhythms from crossing time zones can have a detrimental effect on athletes' health and performance and on the character and competitiveness of the games. The leagues have taken some steps in conjunction with the players to try to mitigate the adverse effects. While helpful, most of the changes appear to address player comfort and some recovery without really dealing with the core problem of sleep deprivation and circadian rhythm changes.

The NBA plays 82 games in 177 days. Players get their own rooms and they get 18 days off during the season where they do not have to travel or conduct promotional activities. The league has tried to reduce the number of back-to-back games and even slightly increased the length of the season. However, it is an uphill battle. Speaking to ESPN in 2018, the coach of the Sacramento Kings at that time, Dave Joerger, said at their away game in Salt Lake City, "We're just trying to survive. Five games in seven nights. Five different cities, three different time zones." They lost that game.

Major League Baseball seems to have the most rules around travel and the timing of games that could take up an entirely different book. They play 162 games, 81 at home and 81 on the road in 182 – 187 days. Most of the games are played in series meaning games are usually scheduled to be played 3 or 4 days in a row in the same city. They are given one day off every 20 days. Players get their own rooms. Although not part of the league rules, it is not uncommon for a starting pitcher to be flown directly home after an away game by himself if he is not scheduled to pitch again during that road trip. This ensures he can rest and not have to deal with the rigours of the additional travel on the road trip.

The NHL, NBA, NFL, and MLB all provide charter flights for their players. Most of the charter flights have "business class" accommodations. The one exception is Major League Soccer in North America. The MLS is a newer league that started in 1996. They do not yet have the revenue to provide the sort of accommodations that players in other leagues enjoy.

They must fly by commercial scheduled airlines and share hotel rooms with other players. They were previously only permitted 4 charter flights per year that are one-way flights, meaning they can fly on charters for 2 games a season. However, they bargained for more in their new CBA. MLS players look around at other leagues and complain about their travel. In July 2019, Graham Ruthven at *The Guardian* reported on the issue and quoted a player from the Philadelphia Union:

> "Should've flown out of Vancouver last night after early kickoff," Alejandro Bedoya tweeted after a Philadelphia Union game earlier this season. "Instead, we wake up at 4:45 am, spend all day in airports (connect in Toronto) & on airplanes w/ no legroom cross country, and just finally landed back in Philly." He sarcastically concluded, "what a great recovery day," punctuated with a facepalm emoji for good measure.

We've Heard It Before

Teams and coaches often consider that sleep is important, but then take the view that athletes (and officials) can simply fight through the consequences of poor sleep by trying harder. Dig in, concentrate, work harder, poor sleep is not an excuse.

However, athletes cannot anymore fight through the effects of poor sleep than they can fight through the effects of poor physical conditioning. Poor physical conditioning and sleep put a ceiling on performance. The only cure for poor physical conditioning is to the take the time and effort to get into shape. The only cure for poor sleep is to take the time and effort to get good sleep.

INCONVENIENT SLEEP

CHAPTER 2

....

Sleep Comes Late to the Science Party

Sleep is an important part of everyone's life. For athletes it can make a difference between winning and losing. However, sleep science is new, and it seems more like it was an afterthought than a concerted, focused effort to uncover the mysteries of sleep.

It took an evolution in scientific discoveries and imagination to get to the point where sleep was even worth studying.

This chapter explores those discoveries and reveals the personalities of the early explorers of sleep. It also shows how many scientific discoveries are really made through trial and error, and sometimes, luck.

*When I woke up this morning my girlfriend
asked me, "Did you sleep good?"
I said, "No, I made a few mistakes."*

Steven Wright

Hippocrates is considered the father of modern Western medicine. Over 2,400 years ago he abandoned the widely held understanding that illness was created by superstition and religious beliefs; rejecting the notion that: you anger the gods and you become ill; you appease the gods and you are cured. Hippocrates believed that illness and disease had natural causes such as environmental, diet and lifestyle factors. He created the first medical school in Greece and established medicine as a profession. His Hippocratic Oath is still administered in Western medical schools. Amongst his many accomplishments is his Book of Prognostics. The first medical textbook to describe the human need for sleep:

> With regard to sleep – as is usual with us in health, the patient should wake during the day and sleep during the night. If this rule be anywise altered it is so far worse: but there will be little harm provided he sleep in the morning for the third part of the day; such sleep as takes place after this time is more unfavorable; but the worst of all is to get no sleep either night or day; for it follows from this symptom that the insomnolency [insomnia] is connected with sorrow and pains, or that he is about to become delirious.

Hippocrates' wisdom about sleep and its affects has not changed much. Despite humans spending about a third of their lives sleeping, sleep medicine would have to wait until late in the 20th century to evolve much past Hippocrates' observations.

The evolution of sleep research and sleep medicine did not occur in a vacuum. Often in science there is an evolution of thoughts and ideas leading to new discoveries. Sometimes new discoveries are the result of thoughtful, organized research. Others are due to pure luck and imagination.

The Rainbow Studies

Humans have always been fascinated by rainbows. They appear after or during rainstorms and sometimes when light shines through a prism or crystal. But what are they and where do the colours come from? The study of rainbows alone would change medicine and our lives forever. The lessons learned from these studies has led to the development of technologies that are used by most professional athletes globally.

Prior to 1665 the prevailing view amongst scientists was that when sunlight entered a prism the prism "coloured" the light and it exited as a mixture of coloured light. However, in 1665 Sir Isaac Newton had a different idea. He thought that the prism was acting more like a filter breaking up sunlight into its various colours. He set out to prove his theory. He conducted what is now considered a child's experiment, but at the time it was ground-breaking.

Imagine Sir Isaac Newton placing a prism in a window exposed to sunlight, then placing a screen far enough away from the prism to separate the colours. He would clearly see red, orange, yellow, green, blue, indigo, and violet light, the colours of the rainbow. Staring at the rainbow he wondered how the different coloured lights were created.

He thought that if the prism acted as a filter breaking up sunlight into its different colours then there must be a way to prove it. He set up his prism and created the rainbow again. He then placed a screen with a small slit in it between the prism and the rainbow. The slit was placed in a way that only allowed the green light through, thus blocking all the other colours. Only the green light came through the prism and was projected onto the screen. He then placed a second prism into the green light coming from the first prism. The screen continued to only show green light.

Newton knew then that he was right. If the prevailing wisdom was correct and prisms merely "coloured" the light coming through it then the green light from the first prism should have been "coloured" when it passed through the second prism. But it did not, only the green light came through the second prism.

We now know that prisms merely act as filters breaking up sunlight into its various colours. It turns out that sunlight is like a pocket full of coins. It is one thing, a pocket full of coins, but it is many things if it is filtered. Take the coins out of your pocket and put them in a coin sorter and give it a shake. You will have various quarters, nickels, dimes and pennies. That is the essence of sunlight; it contains different colours of light, but they have to be filtered in order to see them. Newton's observation that sunlight consisted of many different colours of light would change how scientists viewed nature forever and led to further discoveries that shaped our modern world. Light turned out to have a few more surprises.

In 1800, about 135 years after Newton's discovery, William Herschel became curious about Newton's rainbow of colours and wondered if each colour had the same temperature. Like Newton, he placed a prism so it was exposed to sunlight and the red-orange-yellow-green-blue-indigo-violet light spectrum appeared on the wall. He put a thermometer on each colour to check their temperatures. There was not much difference in temperature in the colours. But then Herschel moved the thermometer to the left of red where there was no visible colour at all – the temperature spiked.

There was an invisible light to the left of the colour red that created a great deal of heat. It later became known as infrared light (below red light). It acted just like light but was invisible to the human eye. This was a new and novel observation. Sunlight contained invisible light as well as visible light! What did this mean? What other invisible light from sunlight might there be?

Johann Ritter became interested in Herschel's discovery. It was known at the time that the normally white compound silver chloride would turn black when exposed to sunlight. A year after Herschel's discovery Ritter devised an experiment to see what colours of the rainbow might be responsible for turning silver chloride black. A prism exposed to sunlight and the rainbow was projected across the room to create the distinct colours. He placed a sample of silver chloride in each of the colours to see what would happen.

He discovered that the silver chloride became darker the closer it came to the violet end of the rainbow. Then he placed some silver chloride outside the right side of the rainbow past the colour violet. The results were dramatic. The silver chloride had turned the darkest of any of the samples. He had discovered a new invisible light ray to the right of the colour violet. He dubbed the new invisible light "Chemical Rays" as they had initiated a strong chemical reaction with silver chloride. This new invisible light would eventually be called beyond violet light or ultraviolet light.

Scientists became very interested in light. Not just sunlight, but artificial or man-made light as well. They were able to produce artificial light in the laboratory by fitting metal electrodes into a glass tube. The glass tube had the air removed by vacuum and then high voltage electricity was attached to the electrodes. The electrodes would glow creating artificial light, not much different from modern light bulbs. It was the study of these artificial light sources that took modern medicine to the next step.

The X-ray Link

In 1865, while the U.S. Civil War was winding down and Americans were grieving the assassination of Abraham Lincoln, a 20-year-old German student, Wilhelm Roentgen, enrolled in the Federal Polytechnic Institute in Zurich to study mechanical engineering. He eventually became the chair of the Physics Department at the University of Wurzburg and by 1895 he was studying light emitted from various vacuum tubes.

One day while working with various vacuum tubes, covered with black paper to prevent the escape of visible light, he noticed something unusual. A screen coated with the chemical barium platinocyanide nearby, lit up – it shimmered. What was causing this strange phenomenon?

Roentgen quickly designed an experiment to see what was going on. He again covered the tube with cardboard to block off the visible light and the known invisible ultraviolet and infrared lights. He then turned off the lights in the room and turned on the electricity. No light could be seen through the cardboard but a nearby screen coated with barium platinocyanide shimmered again. He repeated the experiment several times with the same results.

Roentgen reasoned that an invisible ray had penetrated the glass tubing and the cardboard covering and had caused the coated screen to shimmer in the dark. Roentgen had discovered a new type of invisible ray, a much more powerful and penetrating ray. He dubbed it x-ray as "X" is the mathematical term for an "unknown". The name stuck.

Of course, it was only by chance that he had a screen coated with barium platinocyanide nearby that could light up or shimmer when exposed to x-rays, an unusual and lucky combination. Not only was it lucky that he had the screen nearby, but that he actually noticed the faint shimmering. Perhaps pure luck, but a discovery we now know has had a great influence on modern science.

A few weeks later Roentgen exposed his wife's hand to his new x-rays and produced the first x-ray picture, using a photographic plate to capture the image. Two months later, on December 28, 1895, he published his paper "On a New Kind of Rays" in *Science*. That paper raised eyebrows, excitement, and interest worldwide. Within a year the discovery of x-rays spawned 49 books and over 1,000 articles.

Three weeks after his historic paper was published and 11 weeks after Roentgen's first x-ray of his wife's hand, 14-year-old Eddie McCarthy fell while skating on the Connecticut River and hurt his wrist. He was attended to by Dr. Frost, a Professor of Medicine at Dartmouth Medical School and Medical Director of Mary Hitchcock Hospital. Dr. Frost's brother Edwin was a Professor of Physics and Astronomy at Dartmouth College. Edwin had already read Roentgen's paper and had a similar tube in his laboratory so he thought he would give these new x-rays a try. He decided to assist his brother by testing the new rays described by Roentgen on Eddie McCarthy. They set up the equipment in the Physics Department.

...It was possible yesterday to test the method on a broken arm. After an exposure of 20 minutes the plate on development showed the fracture in the ulna very distinctively.

Edwin Frost

Thus, on January 19, 1896, Eddie McCarthy became the first patient in North America to receive an x-ray, albeit in a physics laboratory. A week after, a New York newspaper, *The Sun,* reported:

> Never in the history of science has a great discovery received such prompt recognition and has been so quickly utilized in a practical way as the new photography which Professor Roentgen gave to the world only three weeks ago. Already it has been used successfully by European surgeons in locating bullets and other foreign substances in human hands, arms and legs and in diagnosing diseases of the bones in various parts of the body.

Of course, by today's standards a discovery like x-rays would never make it, in three weeks, from discovery to clinical use. It would take years, if not decades, to complete clinical trials and government approvals, but that was a different era.

In 1901, Wilhelm Roentgen was awarded the very first Noble Prize in Physics for his discovery of x-rays, and "in recognition of the extraordinary services he has rendered by the discovery of the remarkable rays subsequently named after him." He never took out patents on his discoveries and donated the money from his Nobel Prize to the University of Wurzburg. Roentgen later fell into bankruptcy and died largely penniless in 1923. In keeping with his will all his personal and scientific correspondence were destroyed upon his death.

Roentgen became known as the Father of Diagnostic Radiology, a major branch of medicine. Over the next century radiology evolved from the use of x-rays into the use of ultrasound, MRIs, CT scans and many more modern imaging technologies that have changed the way modern medicine diagnoses and treats disease. All from an accidental observation on a screen covered with barium platinocyanide.

In 2004, the International Union of Pure and Applied Chemistry (the organization that names chemicals), honoured Roentgen by naming element 111 "roentgenium", described as a radioactive element with multiple unstable isotopes. Who wouldn't want that honour?

The Brainwave

While Wilhelm Roentgen was interested in the mysterious invisible rays from his vacuum tube, Hans Berger was interested in telepathy; supposed direct communication between human brains. During his military service in 1892 Hans Berger fell from his horse into the pathway of an oncoming horse-drawn artillery battery. Fortunately, the artillery battery was able to stop in time before running him over, but a young Hans feared for his life. At about the same time his sister, many miles away, had a premonition that Hans was in danger and insisted that their father telegraph him. Her premonition was correct, Hans had been in danger at the very moment his sister had the premonition. That experience changed Berger's life and set him on a long journey of discovery.

Berger firmly believed that some sort of signal had been sent from his brain to his sister's brain, some sort of telepathy. He wanted to find out what was going on. He left the military and set out to explore this phenomenon. After graduating from medical school in 1897 he pursued a career in psychiatry, even working on the front lines during WWI as an army psychiatrist. He returned to academia at Jena University (now the Friedrich Schiller University at Jena) in Germany to pursue his passion – to find those mysterious telepathic signals. Although he was a professor at an esteemed university his colleagues largely thought of him as second rate and a bit of a crank. Imagine thinking that the brain can emit external signals of any kind!

Hans Berger suspected that electrical signals were coming from the brain creating telepathic signals. He set out to build a machine to measure those suspected low-level electrical signals. After much trial and error, he found a commercially available Siemen's recording galvanometer that would be able to record electrical voltages as small as one ten-thousandth of a volt. Berger then devised silver electrodes that would be inserted under a patient's scalp that connected to the galvanometer, allowing measurement of brain electrical activity. He named the machine the electroencephalograph, or EEG. The name stuck and is still used today.

In 1924 he produced the first EEG of a human brain; squiggly lines stretched across a long piece of paper, demonstrating the low-level electrical signals from the brain were indeed real. However, fearing ridicule from his colleagues, who thought little of him, he sat on the discovery for 5 years. Finally, in 1929 he published his paper, the technique for, "Recording the electrical activity of the human brain from the surface of the head." It was met with scepticism and derision. It wasn't until five years later, in 1934, that noted British scientists Edgar Douglas Adrian and B.H.C. Matthews were able to repeat Berger's results. Berger had been right all along. The brain did emit low-level electrical signals.

More than a decade after Berger's first measurement of brain electrical activity EEGs gained widespread acceptance in the scientific community. Berger had not found the telepathic signals he had long sought but did invent the EEG and the ability to see low-voltage electrical signals coming from the brain. Like Roentgen he had discovered something invisible that would lead to great new medical diagnostic and treatment options. Berger's EEG machine would go on to become the cornerstone of our modern-day machines used to measure sleep and to diagnose sleep disorders.

Berger was nominated for a Nobel Prize in 1940, but did not win. Sadly, Hans Berger suffered from depression and on June 1, 1941, he committed suicide by hanging himself in the south wing of his clinic. Ironically, EEGs would go on to become a useful tool in psychiatry for the diagnosis of depression.

The DNA Link

In the early 1900s scientists began to use Roentgen's x-rays to "look" inside other objects besides the human body. They used x-rays to determine the atomic structure of chemicals. They could literally "see" atoms. The first chemical structure to be solved with x-rays was table salt, in 1914. Later x-rays were used to solve the structure of more and more complex molecules, particularly complex biological molecules. If you know the structure of molecules you go a long way to figuring out how they function.

Dorothy Crowfoot Hodgkin was born in 1910 in Cairo, Egypt to parents who were both archaeologists and scholars. She attended school in England and became interested in crystals at the age of 10 and was one of only 2 girls allowed to take chemistry classes, largely reserved for the boys. Like her father, she enrolled at Oxford University. Upon graduation she moved to Cambridge University where she studied for her doctorate under Dr. John Bernal, a pioneer in x-ray crystallography. Dorothy Hodgkin eventually moved back to Oxford and went on to figure out the complex structures of penicillin, Vitamin B12, and insulin, amongst others, using x-rays. She was awarded the Nobel Prize in Chemistry in 1964 for her amazing work using x-rays to "see" inside chemicals and to figure out their actual structures.

Like Dorothy Hodgkin, Rosalind Franklin was drawn to the study of crystals and chemicals using x-rays. She received her doctorate from Cambridge University in 1945. Her thesis was on the physical chemistry of coal. However, Franklin soon abandoned her work in coal to go on to be a major if not a somewhat controversial figure in the discovery of the structure of DNA.

In 2000, Brenda Maddox at *The Guardian* wrote an article, "The dark lady of DNA?" explaining the role and frustrations of Rosalind Franklin in the DNA project:

> In 1950, the head of its biophysics unit, Professor John T. Randall, invited Franklin, working in Paris where she had acquired a fine reputation in X-ray crystallography, to apply her skills at King's [College]. After she accepted, he changed his mind about what she should work on and directed her to working on fibres of DNA. She would have the project to herself, he told her, apart from a research student, Raymond Gosling, and an American temporary assistant. He did not tell her that Wilkins had already done formidable work on DNA and intended to continue. Wilkins was away at the time and never knew the terms of [her] appointment. He believed Franklin was coming to join his team…
>
> Franklin, on arriving at King's [College], realized she had made a terrible mistake. She loathed what she felt was the cold atmosphere of King's [College], where women were not allowed in the senior common room.

At King's College Franklin produced the famous "picture 51" of DNA, described by the famous crystallographer, J.D. Bernal as, "amongst the most beautiful X-ray photographs of any substance ever taken."

At that time the global race to discover the structure of DNA was well under way. The leading contenders were Watson and Crick at Cambridge and Pauling and Corey at Cal Tech. The structure of DNA was critical in understanding how DNA worked and how it was able to accurately replicate itself. Pauling and Corey had suggested a triple helix structure. Watson and Crick knew that was wrong as Watson had seen Franklin's "picture 51" of DNA and knew that DNA was likely a double helix.

How they had come to see that picture is controversial. Franklin's supporters contend that Wilkins showed Watson "picture 51" without Franklin's permission. Others contended that Franklin had instructed her student to show the picture "without condition". In any event, armed with "picture 51" Watson returned to Cambridge and with Crick figured out the structure of DNA, a double helix. This was one of the most important discoveries in modern science.

On March 19, 1953, Francis Crick wrote to his 12-year-old son Michael explaining in detail the discovery of the structure of DNA. He said, "You can understand that we are very excited. We have to have a letter off to Nature in a day or so. Read this carefully so that you understand it. When you come home we will show you the model." He signed the letter, "Lots of love, Daddy".

It is an extraordinary letter outlining, for the first time, the structure of DNA and how it can make exact copies of itself; the fundamental basis of life on earth. All of this by early 1953. Michael Crick, who received the letter as a 12-year-old, eventually sold the hand-written letter at auction in 2013 for about $6 million dollars.

In April 1953, Watson and Crick published their famous paper on the structure of DNA in *Nature*. That issue also featured papers by Franklin and Wilkins on their x-ray pictures of DNA. For their discovery Watson, Crick, and Wilkins won the Nobel Prize for Physiology or Medicine in 1962. Franklin had been left out. Nobel Prize rules only allowed 3 people to be jointly nominated for the prize and the persons nominated had to be alive. Sadly, Rosalind Franklin died of cancer in April 1958. There has been some debate as to whether Franklin would have been nominated over Wilkins had she been alive at the time. We will never know.

The controversy aside, the discovery of the structure of DNA changed our world and our lives forever. Research into DNA exploded. DNA science, for example, has convicted criminals and found others innocent; it has helped in paternity suits and identification of ancestors. It has been used to develop new medicines and to modify food sources; for curing and predicting inherited diseases and numerous other uses. It is fair to say that the discovery of the structure of DNA in 1953 dramatically changed our lives and continues to do so.

In a span of about 300 years scientists had figured out that sunlight contained visible and invisible light; that x-rays could be created by artificial light and could be used to "see" into everything from the human body to minerals and chemicals; that the human brain gives off electrical signals that can be measured and that life itself can be replicated by DNA whose structure was discovered with the help of x-rays.

The Sleep Studies – Finally

While the scientific community was celebrating Watson and Crick's discovery of the structure of DNA in 1953 -- across the Atlantic from Cambridge University, on the second floor of Abbott Hall at the University of Chicago, sleep research was just beginning.

By the 1950s there were tens of thousands of scientists worldwide working in physics, chemistry, biology, mathematics, astronomy, geology, medicine, engineering, social science and many more branches of science. Up until the early 1950s there was only one senior scientist in the world working full-time in sleep research, Nathaniel Kleitman.

Born in Kishinev, Russia in 1895, Kleitman immigrated to the United States at the age of 20 and attended both the City University of New York and Columbia University before completing his Ph.D. at the University of Chicago in 1923. Two years later, in 1925, he joined the faculty there as a physiologist. This was four years before Hans Berger published his much-ridiculed paper (at the time) on the electrical activity coming from the human brain he had discovered with his EEG machine.

Nathaniel Kleitman, at the time, was considered, "the most distinguished sleep researcher in the world". In his 1939 book, "Sleep and Wakefulness" Kleitman summed up his popular theory of sleep:

> Although it is a daily recurring phenomenon, often taken for granted as part of the routine of life, sleep has always aroused speculation on its nature, cause, effect, and whether or not it is a necessary evil. Because the waking state of adults is of longer duration than sleep, and also because it constitutes the only period when overt activities are carried on, the average individual is likely to consider it the sole portion of his existence that "counts" in any way, sleep appearing as a "time out" from the game of living. This popular view of sleep as the antithesis of wakefulness has been traditional since the days of Aristotle.

According to Kleitman at the time, there was simply nothing of interest going on during sleep. You closed your eyes; you fell asleep and your brain went into hibernation. How dull!

Earlier studies by a few researchers noticed differences in EEG brain wave patterns between being awake and being asleep. Sleep EEG patterns were slow rolling high waves and sometimes short bursts or spikes in brain wave electrical activity. Awake EEG were low waves and oscillating waves. You could tell if someone was awake or asleep at that time, but not much more.

Kleitman's views evolved over time as more knowledge became available. It was his persistence, leadership and pioneering work in sleep research that eventually earned him the title, "Father of Sleep Research". He became part of the greatest sleep research discovery with his graduate student who completely blew up Kleitman's old theories on sleep. Kleitman mentored the future leaders in sleep research and was an active sleep researcher until his death in 1999 at one hundred and four years old.

While many major scientific discoveries are made by experienced and prominent scientists, usually with doctorate degrees, sleep might be the exception. The discovery that changed sleep research and opened the world's eyes to what was going on in the brain during sleep was made by a man with only a high school diploma. That man was Eugene Aserinsky.

Eugene Aserinsky was born in Brooklyn, New York in 1921, the son of a dentist. He had a passion for physiology, an inquisitive mind, and a somewhat quirky and independent personality.

Aserinsky was married with a family in the early 1950s when he was accepted into graduate school at the University of Chicago. He just had to find a graduate advisor who would accept him and a field of study that interested him. Not an easy task. His interest was in organ physiology. Most professors in the department of physiology at that time were studying cellular physiology, but that didn't interest Aserinsky. By default, that left him with the study of sleep under Kleitman. At that time sleep research was widely considered the dregs of science. There was simply nothing much going on to study. But, Aserinsky didn't have many choices.

With his resume in hand he knocked on Kleitman's door. Aserinsky was not optimistic. He only had a high school diploma and scattered work experience. He did have numerous college credits to his name, just no college degree. He had been a social science major, but dropped out, then a Spanish language major, but dropped out, then a pre-med student, and eventually a dental student. He dropped out of those as well.

When he wasn't in school Aserinsky spent time in the army as an explosives handler then became a social worker and eventually a supervisor in the Department of Employment Security. But at the age of 29, Aserinsky determined that he needed an advanced degree. He had a passion for discovery and science, and he had a family to feed.

After their conversation, Kleitman accepted Aserinsky as his graduate student working towards a master's degree. Later in his career Aserinsky made a comment that the only real criteria for accepting a graduate student was that they have a heartbeat. Apparently, he passed that test.

Kleitman wanted Aserinsky to work on a project that interested Kleitman. He was fascinated with the relationship between blinking and sleep. He had read an article in *Nature* describing how a physicist had once watched two people fall asleep on a train. He was able to figure out when they would fall asleep based solely on their eyes blinking. Their eyes would blink for a while then they would fall asleep. Once asleep, the blinking stopped. Kleitman wanted Aserinsky to pursue that idea. Aserinsky was more fascinated with why a highly regarded publication like *Nature* would bother to publish such a casual observation. Maybe this sleep research thing wouldn't be so difficult after all.

Kleitman set Aserinsky to work testing a claim that the rate at which one blinked could determine the start of a sleep period. The subjects were babies. The project was tedious. Aserinsky tried but became frustrated. You can measure how often and how fast people blink when they are awake but what about when they are asleep? Aserinsky observed that the eyeballs of babies would sometimes move around when they were asleep. Was that blinking? If it was, how do you measure it? There was simply no proper and accepted description of blinking or how to measure it, particularly when the eyes were closed. It became too confusing. Aserinsky had to tell Kleitman that the "blinking" project was doomed.

Aserinsky proposed that he just consider any kind of eye lid movement instead of just blinking. That would be easier to measure. Kleitman agreed and Aserinsky was back in business, except there was no clearly defined objective for this new project. It involved just staring at sleeping babies looking for eyelid movements. A prospect Aserinsky considered, "as exciting as warm milk". After studying babies' eye movements for months, he was finally able to detect a 20-minute time-period in the baby's sleep cycle when there would be no eye movement and the baby would usually wake up. He impressed the mothers by telling them with almost complete accuracy when their babies would wake up. He described the phenomenon as NEM (No

Eye Movement). The baby project was now over. Not much to learn there and certainly not enough to earn a master's degree.

Kleitman suggested Aserinsky expand his research and study the eye movements in sleeping adults, during an entire night's sleep. He also suggested Aserinsky bypass his master's degree program and embark on a Ph.D. program. The department faculty were not amused. Aserinsky was asking to leap from a high school diploma to a Ph.D. degree! He was eventually able to convince them that he was up to the job as he had numerous college courses to his credit, enough, he said, to challenge the Guinness World Record for such things. The faculty finally acquiesced. Aserinsky was on his way. He knew it was a big gamble. If his research did not result in a Ph.D. he would have wasted many years of research, he would have no college degree at all, and little job prospects.

Aserinsky knew from his observations of babies that there must be some sort of connection between eye movements and sleep. His proposal was quite simple. Study the brainwaves and eye movements of subjects continuously throughout the night and see if any patterns emerged.

Sounds simple enough, except for a few minor problems! It had never been done before and he would need an EEG machine. He also had no budget whatsoever. He had to scrounge. Kleitman offered him an old EEG machine stored in the basement. It turned out the machine was the first hand-made prototype of a commercial EEG machine called an Offner Dynograph. A machine more suited for a museum, than a research lab. Aserinsky would also have to modify the equipment to measure eye movements which had not been done before.

He tinkered for months to get the machine to work properly. It would sometimes randomly show eye movements when there were no eye movements and sometimes even when no one was hooked up to it. He struggled with the problem and once said, "the research project was blowing up before me." He was ready to quit, "Weeks passed as I alternated between despondency and panic." He had to find a way to make it work.

After struggling for weeks, he had a revelation to deal with the machine randomly measuring eye movements in just one eye. He realized that eye movements normally occur simultaneously in both eyes, not as individual movements. If the machine recognized eye movement signals in both eyes at the same time, they would be real and could be counted. Eye movements in just one eye were likely useless artifacts and would not count. He was back in business.

Aserinsky set up his research lab so that a subject could sleep in bed in a dark room isolated from the equipment. The subject was hooked up to his modified EEG machine, layed in bed, and the cords went through the wall into the next room where Aserinsky could monitor the results remotely.

He spent many, many nights conducting EEG and eye movement studies on over 20 patients. "All that was necessary was a compulsive drive to stay up all night and measure miles of pen squiggles." He estimated that each night's data would consume about a half mile of paper. Later in his career Aserinsky joked that his work, "practically made the denuding of the world's timberlands inevitable."

He often used his 8-year-old son, Armond, as a subject. One night he noticed that Armond's EEG and eye movements indicated that he was awake. Aserinsky went into the room to see if Armond was okay, but he was fast asleep. His son's brain

EEGs acted as if he was wide awake, but he was not. His eye movements were rapid. He repeated this experiment many times with the same results. Something was going on.

He had discovered several periods during the night when brain waves would not look like sleeping brain waves, but more like awake brain waves and at the same time the eyes would jerk around rapidly. Aserinsky would later coin the term Rapid Eye Movement sleep or REM sleep to describe that phenomena.

Aserinsky's adult patients also experienced REM sleep during the night. He observed that, on average, rapid eye movement would appear about 3 hours after going to sleep. A second REM period would occur 2 hours after that and a third REM period would emerge at a closer interval. A fourth REM period occurred just before waking up. Most REM sleep occurred within the last few hours of night sleep. He also observed that there were differences in the timing of REM sleep and that even during a REM period subjects went in and out of REM sleep seemingly randomly. However, he found on average, that each REM sleep period lasted about 20 minutes.

He also observed that while subjects were going through REM sleep their respiratory rate would increase compared to the rest of the night's sleep. He used "motion pictures" of two patients to prove that REM sleep was real and could be observed directly. He could show that the brain waves looked like the patients were awake and the "motion pictures" showed the patients' eyes moved rapidly at the same time.

Aserinsky would also wake up patients during REM sleep and ask them about dreaming; 74% of the time they recalled detailed dreams. When he woke up subjects who were not in REM sleep only about 9% could remember dreaming. Eighteen of the subjects were male. Aserinsky observed that the two women in his study had sleep "similar to that obtained by males".

Many years later, in 1987, when Aserinsky was at the School of Medicine at Marshall University he looked back on his work at the time:

> According to my anti-intellectual "Golden Manure" theory of discovery, a painfully accurate, well-focused probe of any minutiae is almost certain to divulge a heretofore unknown nugget of science. This was the philosophy that propelled me to make continuous measures of eye movements while people slept. It was also a credo of desperation.

Aserinsky briefly considered calling REM, "jerky eye movements" which was likely more descriptive but changed his mind to "eliminate humorous connotations."

Aserinsky was ready to publish his findings. It is customary that professors put their name as authors first and the graduate students who did the actual work put their name second. Aserinsky was having nothing to do with that. The paper was published in *Science* on September 4, 1953, entitled, "Regularly Occurring Periods of Eye Motility, and Concomitant Phenomena, During Sleep". Aserinsky's name came first. The paper was less than two pages long. He later described his feelings on the discovery:

> If anything is characteristic about the REM discovery, it was that there was no teamwork at all. In the first place, Kleitman was reserved, almost reclusive, and had little contact with me. Secondly, I myself am extremely stubborn and have never taken kindly to working with

others. This negative virtue carried on throughout my career as evidenced by my resume, which reveals that I was either the sole or senior author in my first thirty publications, encompassing a period of twenty-five years.

Aserinsky was convinced he had completed enough work to be awarded his Ph.D. The faculty did not agree.

Aserinsky's life had not been easy, both professionally and personally. He suffered with poverty, having to borrow money from Kleitman and occasionally steal food to help his family survive. He needed his Ph.D. to get a job. Eventually the faculty made a proposition. He could have his Ph.D. if he could find a job outside the University of Chicago. They would then be done with him. Otherwise he would have to stay, without a degree, and complete a few more years of work on REM sleep and then hope to get his Ph.D.

Aserinsky soon found a job studying salmon at the University of Washington. He received his Ph.D., borrowed $200 from Kleitman and moved to Seattle. He was then lost to the world of sleep research for over a decade. He stayed in Seattle for a year, then took on a faculty position at Jefferson Medical College in Philadelphia studying animal respiration. At that point sleep research was still looked at by the scientific community with a great deal of scepticism. To get the job he claimed that he was only interested in neurophysiology and that his sleep research had, "been a deviant, unfortunate interlude". He later moved to West Virginia and became a professor of physiology at Marshall University. His REM sleep paper in *Science* initially drew little attention. It was not cited by any other researchers until some 2 years after publication.

Sadly, Aserinsky's wife who suffered from depression and was institutionalized, committed suicide. Although his life had not been easy, he never lost his interest in sleep research. Eventually, his son convinced him to write to Kleitman who had, by then, retired from the University of Chicago. Kleitman encouraged Aserinsky to return to his passion studying REM sleep and then reminded his former student that he still owed him a hundred dollars. Such was their relationship. Aserinsky paid his bill.

In March 1963, Aserinsky returned to his birthplace, Brooklyn, to attend a meeting of sleep researchers. An article in the *Smithsonian Magazine* relates a conversation with Aserinsky's son about the meeting, "People were shocked. They looked at him and said, 'My god, you're Aserinsky! We thought you were dead!'" He had been gone that long. In those days there was no social media. If you wanted to communicate you had to telephone or write letters. Aserinsky had little to do with the sleep research community for decades later, until the 1990s.

The *Smithsonian Magazine* article went on to relate conversations with Aserinsky's daughter. In the mid-1990s a fortuitous meeting between Peter Shiromani, an assistant professor of psychiatry at the University of California at San Diego, and Aserinsky's daughter led to an invitation for Aserinsky to address the 1995 meeting of the Associated Professional Sleep Societies in Nashville. She had noticed his licence plate 'REM SLEP' in a parking lot of a Target store and struck up a conversation. "I really like your plates! Did you know my father discovered REM sleep?" It was an OMG moment. He said, "You must be Eugene Aserinsky's daughter!"

Shiromani asked for her father's address and passed it onto colleagues who invited Aserinsky to the scientific meeting. "It was very difficult to get Aserinsky to come, people who knew him in the early days said, 'Don't invite him.'" He had rubbed some people the wrong way.

The Nashville meeting was to honour Kleitman for his 100th birthday. Aserinsky reluctantly attended and addressed the audience of about 2000 researchers. The sleep research community had grown from a handful of people when Aserinsky was in graduate school to many thousands globally.

Aserinsky received two standing ovations. His daughter who accompanied him to Nashville said, "It was one of the high points of his life". "He wore a name tag, and people would stop and point and say, 'There's Aserinsky!'"

Sadly, three years later, at age 77, Aserinsky crashed his car into a tree in Carlsbad, California and was killed. An autopsy could not determine the cause of the accident, although it was widely speculated that he may have fallen asleep at the wheel.

In 2003, on the 50th anniversary of the discovery of REM sleep, the Sleep Research Society erected a large zinc plaque at the University of Chicago Medical Center, adjacent to Abbott Hall where Aserinsky had begun his work in the early 1950s.

"Commemorating the 50th Anniversary of the Discovery of REM Sleep by Eugene Aserinsky, Ph.D., and Nathanial Kleitman, Ph.D., at the University of Chicago".

Aserinsky finally had some recognition. His discovery of REM sleep eventually turned the world of physiology and psychiatry upside down. He was a true explorer of science. He was the catalyst for the modern multi-billion-dollar sleep industry. He saw none of it, but forever changed the way the world viewed sleep. Aserinsky should be remembered as a passionate, independent, inquisitive man who made personal and professional sacrifices for pure discovery.

A leading French sleep researcher, Michel Jouvet, later compared Aserinsky's discovery of REM sleep to "finding a 'new continent in the brain'". This was more than discovering that the brain was active during sleep or that our eyes "jerked around" during several REM episodes at night. This was a whole new state of being. During REM sleep our brains are wide awake but our bodies are frozen, we cannot move during REM sleep, but we dream. Scientists were faced with the enigma of identical EEG brain waves appearing during REM sleep and being awake. How could this be? Scientists were intrigued. There was much work to do.

Michel Jouvet later described the rush to explore REM sleep, "Very seldom in the history of physiology has so much effort been devoted to the description, quantification, classification, and delimitation of such a complex phenomenon of almost totally unknown function."

Discovering a Continent is One Thing But Exploring it is Another.

Before Aserinsky moved to the University of Washington with his newly minted Ph.D., Kleitman had brought on a new graduate student, William Dement.

Born in Wenatchee, Washington in 1928, Dement received his undergraduate degree from the University of Washington before enrolling at the University of Chicago. He had a keen interest in psychiatry, unlike Aserinsky who was a physiologist. At that time the field of psychiatry was very interested in dreams largely because of the influence of the theories of Sigmund Freud that dominated the field of psychiatry at the time. So, the notion that the dream state could be detected by EEG was very attractive to Dement. With his education and keen interest in the subject, Kleitman took on Dement as a graduate student. (He apparently also had a heartbeat, which didn't hurt.)

Aserinsky taught Kleitman and Dement how to conduct the all-night sleep studies using his modified EEG machine. He had been the only one who knew how to do it. One night while Dement was conducting a sleep study by himself on a subject, Aserinsky decided to check in on his pupil and entered the lab. The subject was wide awake but Dement was fast asleep! It was not supposed to work that way.

After Aserinsky moved to Seattle, Dement and Kleitman carried on exploring this new continent in the brain. They knew at the time that EEG brain waves were different when people were asleep and when they were awake. They also knew that during sleep the brain gave off two different kinds of brainwaves and REM sleep. No one knew if there was any pattern to the different brainwaves during sleep or if the differences occurred randomly. Kleitman and Dement decided to find out.

They conducted overnight sleep studies on 33 patients with 162 nights of data. They reviewed the literally miles and miles of squiggles on paper to try to find patterns in the EEG printouts. REM sleep was easily recognized in the subjects, but they found something else. There was a pattern, or patterns, that could be predicted.

They discovered that when people fell asleep their brain soon began giving off EEG electrical signals that were long slow waves. It stayed that way for about 30 minutes. Then the brain waves began to change to much slower waves and had short bursts of electrical activity that showed up as "spikes" on the graph paper. Then the subjects went through REM sleep for about 20 minutes and the cycle repeated. Like all good scientists, Kleitman and Dement applied labels to their observations.

In 1957, Kleitman and Dement published an article (Cyclic variations in EEG during sleep) labelling the sleep stages and REM sleep and describing how brain waves changed throughout each stage. They noted that the cycle of non-REM sleep followed by REM sleep would repeat itself several times during the night. Each cycle would last about 90 or 100 minutes and as the night went on the frequency of REM sleep increased. That 1957 paper defined sleep in a standardized way that has remained largely unchanged today. Until this 1957 paper, sleep was still considered a "single state". They showed it was far from that. A complex mixture of different types of brain waves repeated throughout the night. This discovery opened the eyes of the medical community and spawned sleep research globally.

William Dement was at the forefront of not only pure sleep research but using that research in clinical practice and organizing the medical community to gain credibility in the overall scientific community.

After leaving the University of Chicago in the late 1950s he went to Mount Sinai Hospital where he stayed for a few years before moving to Stanford University in California in the early 1960s. Sadly, William Dement passed away on June 17, 2020, about one month short of his 92nd birthday. He dedicated most of his life to sleep research. He has been dubbed the "Father of Sleep Medicine", a well-deserved title.

As far as we know, the only reason we need to sleep that is really, really solid is because we get sleepy.

William Dement

While more and more researchers became interested in sleep medicine it was Dement who became fascinated with not only "normal" sleep but also with "abnormal" sleep.

Dement's work followed two paths. He continued with his sleep research and by necessity the treatment of people with sleep difficulties. In addition, he led and organized the burgeoning sleep medicine industry. As it was new and there were no standardized approaches or associations or organized research groups.

One of the most visible "abnormal" sleep conditions at the time was narcolepsy, a condition where a person randomly and inexplicably falls asleep. Whether standing in line at a movie theatre, eating in a restaurant, or anywhere else, a person may simply collapse and fall asleep. There was no apparent connection to the activities being carried out; a person just went from being fully awake to being fast asleep no matter where they were.

In January 1963, Dement placed an ad in the San Francisco Chronicle seeking people suffering from the symptoms of narcolepsy. He received over 100 responses. He discovered that only about half the subjects actually had narcolepsy and had not been previously diagnosed with the condition. The other half suffered from sleep issues, just not narcolepsy.

It turns out that narcolepsy is a condition where a person randomly goes from being wide awake directly into REM sleep. During REM sleep the body freezes so the person collapses, dreams, and is fast asleep. Later it was discovered that the condition is caused by a genetic abnormality. Much later, in 1986 another condition called REM sleep disorder was discovered. In that condition a person appears to sleep normally but when they go into REM sleep their bodies do not freeze. Instead, they act out their dreams often thrashing around and injuring themselves and often their bed partner.

During the 1960s sleep research was expanding but the researchers largely used the monitor developed by Aserinsky and sleep staging developed by Kleitman and Dement. However, in 1965, two different groups of researchers independently decided to also measure breathing during sleep. They discovered that disrupted breathing also disrupted sleep. The condition became known as sleep apnea; where a physical restriction in the throat prevents proper breathing which wakes up the person every few minutes making it impossible to get good sleep. It was initially thought to only be associated with obese individuals as their physical size put pressure on their throat and restricted their breathing. Eventually it was determined that sleep apnea could be caused by other factors including jaw structure.

The original discovery of sleep apnea in Europe in 1965 was largely ignored in the United States. It wasn't until Christian Guilleminault, a French Neurologist and Psychiatrist, joined Dement at Stanford University in 1972 that American researchers started to pay attention to breathing and sleep. The way sleep was measured soon expanded. Researchers started to combine the original Berger EEG machine, Aserinsky's eye movements and the French breathing measurements. Later, heart monitors and body movements were added. In 1974, Stanford researcher, Gerry Holland, coined the term, "polysomnography" or PSG, meaning many channels of recorded sleep. The term is now widely used throughout the world.

The Football Connection

In 1973, 12-year-old Reggie White, born in Chattanooga, Tennessee, declared to his parents that he wanted to be two things: a football player and a minister. He went on to accomplish both. In his senior year in high school he was an All-American and the top university recruit in Tennessee. He played at the University of Tennessee where he excelled and was heavily recruited by professional teams.

He was drafted by the U.S. Football League team, the Memphis Showboats, as a defensive player. When that league collapsed two years later, he was picked 4th overall in the first round by the National Football League's Philadelphia Eagles. He played 15 seasons in the NFL as a defensive lineman with the Eagles, and then the Green Bay Packers and eventually the Carolina Panthers. He became an ordained Evangelical minister and earned the nickname the "Minister of Defence". He also became one of the most decorated NFL players of all time. He was a Super Bowl Champion, was selected 13 times to play in the Pro Bowl, a 10 time All-Pro, received multiple awards for NFL defensive player of year and numerous other awards. His jersey number 92 was retired by the University of Tennessee, the Philadelphia Eagles and the Green Bay Packers. Green Bay and Tennessee named streets after him. He was about as successful and famous as any football player could ever hope to be.

He retired after the 2000 season. On the morning of December 26, 2004, one day after Christmas, Reggie White's family called 911. He was rushed from his home in Cornelius, North Carolina to the nearest hospital where he was declared dead at the age of 43.

Reggie White died of cardiac arrhythmia, a complication of sleep apnea. He had suffered from that condition for many years. His wife Sara, (in conjunction with the Sleep Wellness Institute) founded the Reggie White Sleep Disorders Research Education Foundation, dedicated to ensuring all people have access to treatment for sleep disorders, "regardless of their socio-economic status".

A 2017 study found that about 50% of the tested retired NFL lineman suffer from sleep apnea. Today, many sleep disorders are treatable.

The Expanding Sleep Business

Dement and his colleagues became more and more concerned about the number of people they were seeing in their research lab that had "abnormal" sleep or sleep disorders. By 1970 they opened the first sleep lab in the world, using PSG, at Stanford University to diagnose and treat sleep disorders. However, they could only see a handful of patients at a time. The U.S. population in 1970 was over 200 million people. The first sleep lab was a start, but hardly enough.

However, until 1975 Sleep Medicine was considered "experimental" and insurance companies did not cover the testing. After 1975 that changed, and sleep centres began popping up across the country. By 1975 five additional sleep centres had opened in New York, Texas, Pennsylvania and two in Ohio to diagnose and treat patients with sleep disorders.

In 1988, while Reggie White was in his third season with the Philadelphia Eagles and in the prime of his career, Dement became increasingly concerned about the large numbers of people with sleep disorders and the impact on them and on society generally. Dement and a colleague travelled to Washington D.C. to seek government funding for sleep research. They met with Dr. Mona Sarfaty, the health liaison for the senate committee on Health, Education, Labor and Pensions. She asked them "how many individuals were practicing sleep medicine around the United States." She chuckled at their answer, "Your small numbers do not justify such a major legislative step." She suggested, "One route to a more mainstream presence would be the creation of a national commission that would study the impact of your field in society and report the results to the Congress along with recommendations."

A committee was formed and met two years later in 1990. The government would only fund half of the project so Dement had to find private funding for the rest. A donation from the Carnegie Corporation kept the committee afloat. In a hearing in 1992, Senator Hatfield of Oregon described America as a "vast reservoir of ignorance" about sleep. Contrast that with DNA science. By 1988 DNA science was not only a publicly accepted science but was used in criminal investigations and accepted by the courts as scientific evidence.

On January 1, 1995, the American Medical Association recognized Sleep Medicine as a self-designated practice specialty. More and more researchers and physicians from a variety of disciplines became interested in sleep. The number of sleep clinics was growing, but not without its critics.

Writing for the journal *Chest* in 1999, Nancy Collop expressed concern for the lack of standards. What she described at the time sounded like the sleep industry was turning into a bit of a wild west show:

> All of us who have spent a night without sleep know it is an important bodily function. Sleep disorders are common; insomnia affects one third of the population and half of patients with chronic medical conditions such as diabetes, hypertension, and heart disease. Additionally, obstructive sleep apnea syndrome may afflict up to 5% of the adult male population.

> Because of statistics like these, sleep medicine is a burgeoning field. It is unique in that it encompasses both physicians and PhDs in a variety of medical specialties. Pulmonologists pioneered much of the early research in sleep medicine because of their interest in sleep-related breathing disorders. Subsequently, many pulmonologists were involved in developing the standards for accreditation and certification now available for both sleep laboratories and physicians in this field.

> There are many controversies regarding sleep medicine, and several of these directly affect the pulmonologist members of the American College of Chest Physicians (ACCP). Sleep laboratories are opening regularly in this country. What is required to set up a sleep laboratory? Money and a building! Anyone can open a sleep laboratory, and it seems that just about everyone is. In the

small city of Charleston where I reside, there are at least seven sleep laboratories run by a variety of specialists, including ear, nose, and throat; pulmonologists; and neurologists. Many of these physicians do not have any specific training in sleep medicine. There is also a lack of quality control in sleep laboratories. In some labs, technicians "score" the sleep study, and the physician never actually reviews the study, but only develops an interpretation based on the scores. Portable sleep studies are also being performed with even less quality control. What is the reason for the popularity of sleep laboratories? Patients and income. The significance to the pulmonologist is many of these labs are being run by us or are in direct competition with us.

The medical community eventually came together on the issue of sleep medicine. Today there are over 7,500 sleep specialists certified by the American Board of Sleep Medicine. However, there are consequences for sleep coming late to the science party.

General Practitioners in North America normally receive less than 2 hours or so of sleep training in a 4-year medical program. The rationale is that in medical school the curriculum is already 4 years long and cannot be extended. If more sleep medicine was taught what would be kicked out? The result is that most General Practitioners have little training in dealing with sleep issues.

Sleep medicine has made many advances, and much is now known about sleep, but there is also much more that is not known.

Insomnia is a condition where you have trouble falling asleep, staying asleep and sometimes waking up too early. Most people have experienced it, even on a temporary basis. You can't get to sleep, when you do finally fall asleep you tend to wake up a lot and just stare at the ceiling. Such insomnia is often experienced by athletes, particularly when they are anxious about an upcoming event.

There are also chronic sufferers of insomnia. People who report having a hard time getting to sleep and wake up frequently every night. Some studies have shown that about a third of the population exhibits at least one of the symptoms of insomnia. It is a big problem.

One of the many mysteries about insomnia that doctors have noticed over the years is that some patients who report chronic insomnia and undergo PSG in a sleep lab, actually sleep well. PSG shows the patients are good sleepers but in the morning the patients report they didn't sleep well and were awake most of the night! The patients think they slept 2 or 3 hours, but PSG shows they slept 7 hours.

The medical community labelled this condition as "paradoxical insomnia" or "sleep misperception". You think you were awake all night, but you were actually asleep. Why is that?

In 2017, Daniel Kay at Brigham Young University and 10 other colleagues, mostly from the University of Pittsburgh, decided to investigate this mystery a bit further. They recruited 32 normally healthy people with chronic insomnia and 30 who were good sleepers. Each person's sleep was measured with PSG and then each person reported how they thought they slept. However, they also did something more revealing. While the subjects were sleeping and undergoing PSG, the researchers used an advanced brain scan technique to look at which parts of the brain were active while the patient was sleeping or attempting to sleep.

The subjects who said they had poor sleep and were awake all night, but where their PSG brainwaves actually showed they were asleep, had interesting brain activity. During non-REM sleep their brains were quite active in regions associated with "conscious awareness". This means, the part of the brain that tells you that you are awake was quite active when the brain was actually asleep. The brain was asleep but telling the subject they were awake. Very odd!

This demonstrates some of the complexities of our brain and sleep. New sleep research is published almost daily showing how sleep affects many human functions. That should not be too surprising. Our brains are like a computer CPU. If your CPU malfunctions or is damaged, you shouldn't be surprised if most, or all, of your programs are adversely affected.

It is unfair to say that sleep research is in its infancy, but it may very well be barely out of diapers. While sleep research has evolved over the years and has made some impressive gains, it seems that the current state of sleep research is not much different from Sir Isaac Newton just staring at a rainbow wondering what it is all about and where it will lead. There is so much more to learn.

CHAPTER 3

The Science-ish Theory

Science is largely an evolution of ideas, many of which take decades and longer to prove or disprove. In addition, science does not operate in a vacuum. It can be influenced by business and sometimes the desires of the community. We live in a world where there is a desire for quick fixes and simple solutions to complex problems. The result can be the production of fraudulent products and/or fraudulent ideas to perpetuate sales.

Athletes are not immune and can be subjected to products that may create more harm than good.

One time a cop pulled me over for running a stop sign. He said, "Didn't you see the stop sign?" I said, "Yeah, but I don't believe everything I read."

Steven Wright

Every year in the United States golfers lose over 300 million golf balls, enough to fill about 600 buses. Lost golf balls are the bane of golfers. Looking up into trees, stomping through tall grass or knee deep in water, looking for balls is all part of the game—just not the fun part.

Mercifully, official golf rules only give you 3 minutes to find your ball. After that it is officially "lost" and you get to take out your next (soon to be lost) golf ball and play on. It seems that only the golf ball manufacturers are happy to have you lose them. It is no wonder companies have tried to find creative ways to help golfers find their lost golf balls.

As novelty items go the "Golf Ball Finder" was quite clever. It consisted of a small, empty plastic box with an attached handle to hold it upright, much like a handgun. An antenna from an old 1960s style radio was attached on a swivel to the front. Holding the Golf Ball Finder in your hand, pointed in the direction you hit the ball, the antenna would swing around and hopefully point to a golf ball.

A brochure at the time explained how the Golf Ball Finder worked:

> It is tuned to home in to the elements found in all golf balls. Please don't ask us the theory of its operation.

That's the main reason we have not applied for patents which would expose this technology. It's also a great novelty item that you should have fun with especially for the golfer who has "everything"!

With the millions of golf balls lost each year it is not hard to imagine pointing the Golf Ball Finder anywhere on a golf course and eventually finding a ball, especially if it points to water hazards. Not bad for a $20 investment. Recovered golf balls are a lot cheaper than buying new ones.

However, Wade L. Quattlebaum, an ex-car salesman from South Carolina, found a better use for the Golf Ball Finder. He formed a company called Quadro Corporation that made a similar product, called the Quadro Tracker. It was designed, not only to find golf balls, but also to detect drugs, weapons, explosives and specific people (if you had a picture of them). To heck with finding golf balls, this new detector could find almost anything. Quadro Corporation hailed it as a "breakthrough in modern physics".

Even in a pre-9/11 world, there was a market for such a device. Many thought it would be very helpful to have a simple to use instrument that could quickly find explosives, weapons, and drugs. The Quadro Tracker sold between $400 and $8000 per unit and was marketed to school districts, law enforcement agencies and prisons and customs border agencies.

Quadro Corporation alleged that the device contained a preprogrammed chip:

> The frequency chip is oscillated by static electricity produced by the body inhaling and exhaling gases into and out of the lung cavity. This static electricity is propagated on the surface of the body to the tracker

which utilizes the charge to oscillate the chip.

On April 22, 1996, a U.S. District Court judge, granted a permanent injunction barring Quadro Corporation and its principals and agents from marketing or selling the Quadro Tracker or similar devices. After demonstrating that the devices, simply put, did not work, the court agreed with Plaintiff's expert testimony stating, "the devices could not possibly locate objects as represented by defendants under any known principles of modern science." It was, in reality, an empty plastic box fitted with a transistor radio antenna. The preprogrammed chips were, "small pieces of polymer coated paper run through a copy machine and sealed between two pieces of plastic."

Unfortunately, about 1,000 Quadro Trackers were sold across 16 states. The *Tampa Bay Times* reported that Robert Hobbs, commander of the county narcotics task force in Beaumont, Texas, paid $3,250 for a Quadro Tracker and later said, "Yeah, I've got a little egg on my face on this one. But in a way it's good that it happened to law enforcement, because it keeps our perspective in order and makes us more sympathetic to victims."

Further, the *Tampa Bay Times* reported:

> The police weren't the only group interested in the Tracker. School districts and prisons bought some, too.
>
> In Florida, Polk County schools spent nearly $2,700 for three units, and Glades County sheriff's deputies bought one.
>
> Seminole County's school system spent $49,750 to buy Trackers for each of its 50 schools.
>
> Around the country, at least 30 school districts from

Pennsylvania to Texas have bought Trackers, according
to the School Board News.

It Gets Worse

Jim McCormick, a British business man, had an even better
use for the Golf Ball Finder and a much more lucrative one.
He formed a company called Advanced Tactical Security &
Communications Ltd., took the Quadro Golf Ball Finder idea,
relabelled it ADE 651 and marketed it as a bomb detector to
military forces in the Middle East and Far East. The ADE 651
sold for as much as $60,000 a piece, after the U.S. Federal Court
had granted a permanent injunction against the sale of the
Quadro Tracker in the United States.

McCormick's largest customer was the Iraqi government who
paid over $85 million for the ADE 651s for use in hundreds
of police and military checkpoints. The results were disastrous
as the devices could not detect anything and vehicles with
explosives were allowed to pass through, many exploding in
populated areas. In 2010, BBC Newsnight exposed the fraud and
the U.K. quickly banned the ADE 651 from export to Iraq and
Afghanistan. In 2013, Jim McCormick was convicted of three
counts of fraud in London and sentenced to 10 years in prison.

Most telling was the comment made to the BBC by McCormick
that the device "does exactly what it's designed to – it makes
money."

Fake products or pseudo-science were hardly invented by the
makers of the golf ball finders-turned bomb detectors and are
not always meant to be so deceptive. Some things are just hard

to prove or disprove. Like whether someone is telling the truth or not.

To Tell the Truth

William Moulton Marston was born in Massachusetts in 1893 and later attended Harvard University where he received a law degree in 1918 and then a PhD in Psychology in 1921. He became quite famous in two diverse fields, one involving science, the other arts.

In his early academic life Marston had a keen interest in forensic science and finding ways to figure out if someone was lying or not - the holy grail of law enforcement. His wife, Elizabeth, once told him that when she got excited or mad, she noticed that her blood pressure would rise. That gave Marston an idea. If someone was lying their body should react with guilt and, therefore, possibly, their blood pressure would rise. He decided to test his theory.

He placed a standard blood pressure cuff on various subjects and asked them questions. After each question, he would check their blood pressure. Any increase might indicate they were lying. He tried this method on about 100 criminal cases in Boston and concluded that he was right 97% of the time. There is, however, no indication of how he figured out if any of the "criminals" in the cases had been lying. Perhaps they all had denied being involved with crimes but were later convicted. In any event, Marston was convinced that when people were lying their blood pressure increased.

Marston was invited to use his blood pressure machine by the defence in a murder case in Washington, D.C. James Frye had been charged with shooting and killing a wealthy doctor in 1920. He confessed to the murder, but his lawyers wanted to prove he was innocent. They arranged for James Frye to take the blood pressure test from Marston and he passed! He was innocent, if only they could convince the court to accept that evidence.

In his book, "The Lie Detector Test," Marston told the story of his involvement in the case:

> No one could have been more surprised than myself to find that Frye's final story of innocence was entirely truthful! His confession to the Brown Murder was a lie from start to finish.

The trial began on July 17, 1922, before Judge William McCoy. Frye's defence rested on the evidence of Marston and his machine. The admissibility of Marston's evidence was questioned. The jury heard that Marston was going to testify that Frye had passed his blood pressure test and was therefore innocent. (Today juries are normally excluded from hearing arguments about which evidence is admissible in a trial, for obvious reasons.)

Ultimately, Judge McCoy ruled that the blood pressure test and Marston's evidence were inadmissible. After a four-day trial, Frye was convicted of second-degree murder and sentenced to life in prison. The jury had spared him from the death penalty. Some believe that because the jury had heard Marston was going to testify that Frye was innocent based on his machine, the jury did not recommend the death penalty as they had some lingering doubts. Frye appealed his murder conviction.

The Circuit Court of Appeals in the District of Columbia upheld the conviction and the dismissal of the blood pressure evidence.

That decision set out what became known as the famous "Frye" legal test for the admission of "scientific evidence" into court, stating:

> Just when a scientific principle or discovery crosses the line between the experimental and demonstrable stages is difficult to define. Somewhere in this twilight zone the evidential force of the principle must be recognized, and while courts will go a long way in admitting expert testimony deduced from a well-recognized scientific principle or discovery, the thing from which the deduction is made must be sufficiently established to have gained general acceptance in the particular field in which it belongs.

> We think the systolic blood pressure deception test has not yet gained such standing and scientific recognition among physiological and psychological authorities as would justify the courts in admitting expert testimony deduced from the discovery, development, and experiments thus far made.

Marston went on to a teaching career at the American University in Washington, D.C. and Tufts University in Massachusetts. He then moved to California in 1929 to work for Universal Studios as its Director of Public Services, and eventually partnered with Max Gaines, a publisher in the comic book industry. Marston ended up creating Wonder Woman, an iconic superhero. Her symbol was the "Lasso of Truth" which made all those that encircled it tell the truth.

The Larson Model

While Marston's instrument was based on blood pressure alone, a contemporary of Marston, John Augustus Larson, had a better idea. Born in Nova Scotia, Canada, his family soon moved to New England where he eventually attended Boston University. There he earned a Master of Arts degree and had a keen interest in forensic science. His thesis was on fingerprint identification. Larson then moved to the West Coast and by 1920 he had earned a Ph.D. in physiology from the University of California at Berkeley. He worked part-time with the Berkeley Police Department while in school and obtained a full-time job with them after graduation.

Larson worked on improving Marston's blood pressure machine adding measurements for pulse rate and respiration (breathing). Then he figured out how to continuously and simultaneously measure all of those factors. His theory was that when people lie their blood pressure, heart rate, and breathing would all increase. Now to prove it.

His idea was that you simply hook a person up to the polygraph machine and ask them some simple questions, like "do you like college?" or "do you dance?" so the machine could measure baseline data to show how you react when telling the truth. Then the questions would become more pointed addressing issues around a particular crime. If his theory was correct then the person's breathing, heart rate, and blood pressure would all increase when they lied. He soon had a case to test his theory.

Known in Berkeley as the "College Hall" case, some jewellery had been reported missing and presumably stolen from a college dorm room. The police suspected an inside job and brought in all 14 women from the dormitory for questioning while being hooked up to the polygraph machine. The first person Larson tested was Margaret Taylor, the alleged victim. She passed the polygraph test. One by one the other women passed the test. Finally, one woman noticed that her answers to the questions had set off the instruments. She halted the test and bolted out of the police station. She later returned and confessed to the robbery. Larson's polygraph had worked ... sort of. At the very least, it scared the alleged robber into confessing. A year later he married Margaret Taylor, the victim in the case. All in all it was a successful first test of the polygraph machine!!

After the "College Hall" case Larson found much more serious work to do – the high-profile murder of a priest in San Francisco. William Hightower, an apparent drifter, had been charged with the crime. The paper, *The San Francisco Call and Post*, arranged to have Larson test Hightower with his new polygraph machine. The results indicated that Hightower was guilty. The newspaper then splashed all the details and the results across its front page: "Science Indicates Hightower's Guilt".

Hightower went on trial and was convicted of murder—not based on Larson's polygraph test, but on significant physical evidence. Hightower had led the police to the priest's buried body and even knew which direction the body was buried before digging began. In addition, blood and other evidence was discovered at Hightower's residence. He was sentenced to life at San Quentin prison but was paroled in 1965 at the age of 86.

Coincidentally, Larson died in 1965, at the age of 72. In 2003, the Encyclopaedia Britannica Almanac named the polygraph as one of the 325 greatest inventions. Today, Larson's original polygraph is in the Smithsonian Institute in Washington, D.C.

The Marketing of the Polygraph

August Vollmer, the Chief of Police in Berkeley at that time, became a strong advocate and fan of the "lie detector". If not for Vollmer's support, it may very well have faded into history, being only a good local story in California. Vollmer, however, became a leader and icon in U.S. national law enforcement and the lie detector benefited from his support as he took up the torch from Marston and Larson. He became known as the "Father of American Policing".

When Vollmer became the Chief of Police in Berkeley in 1909 there was little structure in policing in America. He changed all that by:

- Putting officers on bicycles, motorcycles and then in cars equipped with radios

- Creating centralized police records

- Insisting on a scientific approach to crime investigations

- Starting a police school, the world's first

- Requiring officers to have college degrees

- Becoming the first chief of police to use fingerprints to identify suspects

- Hired the first female officer in America and one of the first African-American officers

Vollmer also became active in the academic community promoting law enforcement education. He founded the School of Criminology at the University of California Berkeley and was awarded the Public Welfare Medal from the National Academy of Sciences. He was also elected the President of the International Association of Chiefs of Police. In a meeting of that association, in 1922, he had Larson demonstrate the lie detector to them.

Furthermore, the American Society of Criminology created the "August Vollmer Award" to recognize, "an individual whose scholarship or professional activities have made outstanding contributions to justice and/or to the treatment or prevention of criminal or delinquent behavior."

By any standard Vollmer was a highly respected pioneer in law enforcement and had a great influence on that community. His strong reputation gave Larson's lie detector a great deal of credibility. The technology was not just local, but now had a national reputation backed by Vollmer's new approach to criminology and his international reputation.

"Lie detectors" became part of the DNA of American law enforcement. It was the "silver bullet" they needed to help detect lies and catch criminals.

The Lie Detector – The Truth Comes Out

In the early 1980s, five women, mostly sex workers, were found dumped along the Green River in Washington State, and the number of murders was increasing. The county police soon created the Green River Task Force to investigate. In 1982, Gary Ridgway, a truck spray painter, was arrested on charges related to prostitution in the area. He soon joined the list of suspects in the murders. In 1984, he was brought in to take a polygraph test and passed, not guilty!

Seven years later, in 2001, Ridgway was arrested and initially charged with four of the murders, based on DNA evidence. Ultimately, he confessed to 48 murders. He was sentenced to 48 life sentences. The police believe he murdered over 70 women – many after he passed the 1984 polygraph test.

The polygraph test had the opposite effect when it was used in a different case. On the morning of September 16, 1986, Bill Wegerle left for work from his home in Wichita, Kansas. His wife, Vicki, was at home caring for their two-year-old son. On his way home for lunch that day Bill saw his wife's car drive by, but she was not driving, someone else was! At his home he found his son, apparently all alone, but then found his wife, tied up and strangled in their bedroom. He called the police.

Bill Wegerle soon became a suspect in the murder. He took two separate polygraph tests and failed both. He must be guilty. However, the police had no other evidence linking him to the crime and he was not charged. For the next 18 years he lived under a cloud of suspicion from the police and the community who suspected he had murdered his wife. Had Bill Wegerle gotten away with murder?

In March 2004, a letter arrived at a Kansas newspaper, the *Wichita Eagle*, which contained photographs of the crime scene and a copy of Vicki Wegerle's driver's license which had been missing since the murder. The return address was purportedly from Bill Thomas Killman. The police later determined that the letter came from Dennis Rader, a Cub Scout leader and church president in the area. Rader was eventually convicted of 10 murders through DNA analysis, including the murder of Vicki Wegerle and sentenced to 175 years in prison. He became famously known as the BTK killer. Bill Wegerle had been innocent all along but had 18 years of his life destroyed from failed polygraph tests.

In 1998, the majority of the U.S. Supreme Court in the case *United States v. Scheffer* stated, "There is simply no consensus that polygraph evidence is reliable".

In 2003, the National Academy of Sciences published a 416-page report on, "The Polygraph and Lie Detection." They were not impressed! They decided the research backing the polygraph was weak and poorly designed.

The American Psychological Association summed it up in their article, "The Truth About Lie Detectors (aka Polygraph Tests)":

> The accuracy (i.e., validity) of polygraph testing has long been controversial. An underlying problem is theoretical: There is no evidence that any pattern of physiological reactions is unique to deception. An honest person may be nervous when answering truthfully and a dishonest person may be non-anxious.

The lie detector is still used extensively in American police investigations and for U.S. federal government and law enforcement screenings and pre-employment screenings. However, courts generally still don't accept the results of polygraph tests, some 90 plus years after its invention.

Polygraphs are not some obscure snake oil product peddled to unsuspecting buyers. Polygraphs have been discussed and reviewed by scientists and reputable organizations for well over half a century. While the supporting science has always been weak, what has largely driven the industry is a desire for a holy grail, a way to fix the age old problem of determining if someone is lying or not. It was driven by those that wanted it to work and needed it to work. It doesn't work.

Poor sleep is endemic in our modern society. Many people, including athletes, long for simple solutions. They want and need something to work. That can make them blind to the actual science. There are parallels to what happened in the polygraph industry.

Sleep Supplements

On February 6, 2018, Lee Jenkins, an experienced NBA writer for *Sports Illustrated* (SI), published an all too familiar article. The story, this time, just happened to involve the Denver Nuggets. Like most NBA teams they are interested in how sleep affects their team and what they can do about it. So, they invited a local sleep doctor to talk to the team for 30 minutes about the importance of sleep and how to improve sleep with sleep hygiene.

One of the players, Trey Lyles, like many other athletes, was concerned that his sleep was inadequate. He felt that he suffered from insomnia and had difficulty falling asleep after games. Lyles wanted to improve the situation. He reached out to the team's head strength and conditioning coach, Felipe Eichenberger for help. The coach introduced Lyles to a new drink, not yet on the market at that time, called Som Sleep, advertised as NSF Certified for Sport. (NSF International certifies that sports supplements do not contain prohibited chemicals. They do not certify that those products actually perform as advertised.)

Lyles began drinking cans of the product and proclaimed, within a month, that he had more than doubled his rebounds and points per game. The article says that after games Lyles would fall asleep at 1:30 am and not at his usual 3 or 4 am. This was a huge improvement, both in his sleep and in his performance on the basketball court.

Other NBA players were paying attention and the manufacturer shipped cases of the product to various NBA teams for the players. The product is now available to the public. Their website says Som Sleep contains magnesium and Vitamin B6 for "Nutritional support for biosynthesis", L-Theanine and GABA to "promote relaxation" and melatonin to "maintain a normal sleep cycle", all "backed by science".

The Som Sleep website states, "We all deserve a better night's sleep. Som Sleep is engineered to help you fall asleep faster and sleep better throughout the night."

The SI article largely dealt with the issue of insomnia in the NBA and touted Som Sleep as a solution. The four ingredients in the product are interesting but none of them can get you to sleep an hour or two faster, or perhaps, even at all. It is worth looking at the scientific evidence of each ingredient.

Magnesium and Vitamin B6

Magnesium is a mineral in the body and is associated with over 300 enzyme systems and other biological functions. Magnesium is found in many food sources such as spinach, cereal, nuts, etc. According to the U.S. National Institutes of Health (NIH) magnesium deficiency is uncommon in healthy people.

In addition, the NIH states that vitamin B6 is found in a wide variety of food. "The richest sources of vitamin B6 include fish, beef liver and other organ meats, potatoes and other starchy vegetables, and fruit (other than citrus). In the United States, adults obtain most of their dietary vitamin B6 from fortified cereals, beef, poultry, starchy vegetables, and some non-citrus fruits." The NIH adds that vitamin B6 deficiency is also uncommon in the United States and is usually restricted to individuals who have impaired renal function, those with autoimmune disorders and those that are alcohol dependent. NBA players tend to be quite young and healthy and most NBA teams provide nutritional support to their players, including the Denver Nuggets. It hardly seems necessary for young, healthy athletes to take magnesium or vitamin B6 supplements.

L-Theanine

L-Theanine is a component of green tea and is marketed as a product that is often associated with the apparent calming effects of green tea. It has been the subject of a number of studies and reviews. In 2011, the European Food Safety Authority (EFSA) published a "Scientific Opinion" on the health claims related to L-Theanine.

The scientific panel at the EFSA determined that none of the claims could be substantiated. With respect to the claim that L-Theanine promotes relaxation the panel determined that it could not draw any positive conclusions from the few studies on the subject. The panel also concluded that there was no evidence of improved cognitive function.

However, it said that two of the studies showed that "reaction time was significantly longer after consumption of L-Theanine than after consumption of [a] placebo." They did not say how long that effect would last. But why would an athlete take a product that might make their reaction time worse for an unspecified amount of time?

There is little evidence on whether L-Theanine can actually reduce stress, but regardless of whether it does, or doesn't, there is simply no evidence L-Theanine as a supplement helps people fall asleep faster or sleep longer.

GABA

GABA (an acronym for gamma-aminobutyric acid, if anyone cares) is also touted as a chemical that will promote relaxation and thus help people get to sleep faster.

When our brain cells talk to each other they emit low-level electrical signals (aka Berger's brainwaves). GABA is a natural chemical that slows down the transmission of electrical signals or blocks some of them altogether. Thus, GABA acts a bit like a "go slow" sign in the brain. The theory is that if you can get more GABA into your brain it will encourage your brain to "slow down" even more and help you to get to sleep faster.

The problem is that the human brain is quite fussy about what it lets in. Not everything we breath, eat, or drink ends up in our brains. Some studies say that GABA cannot cross into the brain from the blood stream, others suggest that GABA can cross into the brain, but at low levels.

One small study of 40 people with insomnia showed that they could get to sleep 13.4 minutes faster than usual when they took 300 mg of GABA. Som Sleep contains a blend of 357 mg of L-Theanine, GABA, and melatonin combined. They do not say how much GABA is in their product as it is "proprietary". However, even if taking 300 mg of GABA could help people fall asleep 13.4 minutes faster, is it really worth it?

Melatonin

Interestingly, the SI article did not mention that the Som Sleep drink contains melatonin, but did state that the NBA player, "craved something stronger than melatonin supplements but healthier than ZzzQuil pills, which left him groggy in the morning." According to the manufacturer's website Som Sleep contains 3 mg of melatonin in each can.

Melatonin is a natural hormone produced in the brain. It is often referred to as the "sleep" hormone or the "Dracula" hormone, as it only comes out in the dark. The brain circulates the hormone throughout the body largely sending messages to various organs and systems that it is nighttime and they should prepare accordingly for sleep. Natural melatonin levels in our bodies are affected by light exposure. At night melatonin levels rise and then fall in the morning.

The manufacturer's website contains many testimonials, including a quote from *Business Insider,* about the effectiveness of its drink, Som Sleep, "Within about 20 minutes I was noticeably drowsy. I crawled over to bed, was asleep within seconds, and slept fully through the night."

In summarizing the research, The National Sleep Foundation says, "For some people, melatonin seems to help improve sleep.

However, when scientists conduct tests to compare melatonin as a "sleeping pill" to a placebo (sugar pill) most studies show no benefit of melatonin."

There are currently no studies showing that Som Sleep improves sleep. Like many suppliers of supplements they rely on anecdotes and testimonials, not scientific research.

The Bigger Picture

Melatonin is widely known and used in North America. From 2007 to 2012 the use of melatonin doubled. It is currently estimated that more than 3.1 million people use melatonin in the U.S.

With such widespread use, there has been an uptick in research on the topic. There are literally thousands of research papers published on melatonin. According to the American Association for the Advancement of Science, "In the last five years alone, more than 4,000 studies using melatonin have been published. Almost 200 of those were randomized clinical trials."

Melatonin is also the only hormone not regulated in the United States. Because it is found naturally in some foods it is treated as a food supplement rather than a medicine. It is different in Europe. Denmark and the Czech Republic prohibit melatonin in supplements. Belgium and Germany allow up to 0.3 mg, any more and the product would be considered a medicine. In Spain and Italy melatonin is authorized as a food supplement only up to 1 mg per day. In the United Kingdom melatonin is not permitted as a food supplement and, at any dose, is considered a medicine available only by prescription from a doctor.

In February 2018, the Director General of France's regulatory agency (ANSES) issued a report on the potential adverse effects of melatonin. It concluded that anyone who takes melatonin should do so only after consulting a doctor. ANSES was concerned that melatonin could interact in a negative way with other medications; that there are no long-term studies on the effect of melatonin and that melatonin should only be taken occasionally and only up to a maximum of 2 mg per day. Finally, ANSES recommended that children and adolescents not consume any supplements containing melatonin. Many amateur and professional athletes are adolescents.

Besides the alleged sleep benefits of melatonin, it is also touted as a way for athletes to overcome jet lag. The National Sleep Foundation noted, "Evidence that melatonin can reset the body clock is more well established, although it is not clear whether exposure to light may be more effective." Translation: There is some research that shows melatonin can help with jet lag, but you are probably better off just getting exposed to light during the day.

Another important issue is dose. How much melatonin should athletes take (assuming it works)? The research is mixed. In 2011, the European Food Safety Authority suggested the research indicated that a dose of 1 mg of melatonin would be needed to get the benefit of falling asleep faster. Other research shows that somewhere between 0.5 mg and 3 mg may be effective. The research is still all over the map. There is simply no consensus on the effective dose of melatonin.

What makes the matter more confusing is that recent research indicates the labelling on most bottles of melatonin is simply wrong. If athletes take melatonin, they might not even know how much they are taking. A 2017 study by colleagues Erland and Saxena, looked at the actual content of melatonin in 30 over-the-counter melatonin supplement products. They discovered that 71% of the products were not even within ± 10% of the advertised melatonin content. Amongst those products tested, melatonin levels varied from 83% below the advertised level to 478% above it. In addition, some samples contained undeclared serotonin which could "lead to serious adverse reactions."

Perhaps more shocking to athletes; the University of California – Berkeley sent out a press release in 2005 announcing some new research: "Melatonin shrinks bird gonads. What does the popular supplement do in humans?"

They raised the issue that melatonin might very well affect humans in the same way. "If melatonin can do this on one neuropeptide system, it has the potential to do it on any other neuropeptide system." The researcher, George Bentley was pretty blunt in his assessment of melatonin:

> It really amazes me that melatonin is available in any pharmacy. It is a powerful hormone, and yet people don't realize that it's as 'powerful' as any steroid. I'm sure that many people who take it wouldn't take steroids so glibly. It could have a multitude of effects on the underlying physiology of an organism, but we know so little about how it interacts with other hormone systems.

Athletes should consider if taking melatonin is worth the risk. It would seem that many of the supplements that athletes are exposed to are 95% marketing and hype, 5% fluff and the rest — science.

How Long Does It Take for you to Fall Asleep?

There have been a number of what are called "meta-analysis" on melatonin. Studies where scientists look at all the published data, sift through them and figure out which ones are relevant and good studies. They analyse the information and come to a consensus on what is known about the product.

A meta-analysis on melatonin in 2005 found that the studies showed subjects would fall asleep 11.7 minutes faster after using melatonin. (Not falling asleep within 11.7 minutes, just falling asleep 11.7 minutes faster than they normally would.) However, they concluded that being able to fall asleep 11.7 minutes faster was "clinically unimportant".

A similar meta-analysis on melatonin in 2013 looked at 19 studies involving 1,683 subjects and concluded that melatonin helped the subjects fall asleep 7.06 minutes faster. In addition, they said melatonin increased sleep time by 8.25 minutes a night.

There are many products on the market that purport to help people get to sleep faster. But this raises an important question. How do you know that you fall asleep faster? Do you know exactly when you are going to fall asleep tonight? Probably not. Then if you took some potion how do you know that you fell asleep faster? You don't.

How long it takes to fall asleep is called sleep latency and is measured in minutes. It has to have a beginning and an end. The end is when you actually fall asleep, that's the easy part. Trying to figure out the beginning is when it gets tricky.

Sleep is not an on/off switch. You are not awake one second and asleep the next. It is a process. Usually, in the beginning stages there is a period of inactivity. Just lying in bed with little movement. This is followed by a period of decreased muscle tone. In this pre-sleep stage people will drop whatever they might be holding in their hands. Then they fall asleep.

When sleep latency is measured using PSG a person is often considered to have fallen asleep when they enter stage 1 sleep as measured by their brainwaves. Interpreting the changes in brainwaves from being awake to being in stage 1 sleep is both an art and a science. However, even with some leeway, when someone falls asleep can normally be measured accurately, within a few minutes. That's the easy part. Trying to figure out when you might start to fall asleep is harder.

When do you Start to Fall Asleep?

If you wake up at 8 in the morning and fall asleep at 8 at night, then theoretically it took you 12 hours to fall asleep. But that is not how the concept is used in sleep medicine.

In sleep medicine, sleep latency or how long it takes you to fall asleep, is a relatively important measurement. It is vital to sleep doctors for two reasons. First, the information is used to assist in diagnosing certain sleep disorders. The longer it takes you to fall asleep the more likely it is you may have insomnia or some other related sleep disorder.

There is also an economic reason. If you routinely fall asleep around 10 at night, then the doctors do not want you to show up at their clinic at 7 to be tested. They would have to pay staff to be there when you are awake, just waiting around until you fall asleep. They want patients to show up just before their normal bedtime.

The general process is that patients come to the sleep clinic ahead of when they would normally fall asleep and are hooked up to the instruments that measure brainwaves, motion, breathing, etc. (PSG). Then the sleep technician turns off the lights in the room, leaving the patient alone in a dark room. This starts the clock ticking to decide how long it takes to fall asleep. Sleep latency is the difference between when the lights are turned off and when you actually fall asleep.

Researchers at the San Joaquin General Hospital in California described the difficulty with the issue:

> Sleep latency is the time in minutes from 'lights out' that marks the starting of total recording time to the first epoch scored as sleep. Sleep latency also indicates if reasonable attention was paid to the patient's sleep diary and the 'lights out' time was close to the patient's routine bedtime at home. Clearly, if the lights are turned out earlier than the patient's usual bedtime, sleep latency would be spuriously long, and the patient may not fall asleep until his/her usual sleep time is reached. Similarly, if the 'lights out' time is later than the patient's usual bedtime, the patient will be sleepy and a spuriously short sleep latency will be recorded. It is of utmost importance that the patient's usual habitual sleep time is incorporated into the patient's sleep study design and 'lights out' time is approximated.

If you are going to say that some product helped a person fall asleep faster, you have to have some objective or reasonable measure of when they were meant to fall asleep in the first place. The University of Pittsburgh School of Medicine became concerned about how they would figure that out. The researchers went back and looked at more than 1,700 overnight sleep studies to determine the difference between when patients said they would normally fall asleep and when they actually fell asleep according to their brainwave (PSG) measurements.

They discovered that patients were very bad at predicting when they would fall asleep, based on memory alone. So, they asked their patients to keep a sleep log. That is, the patients were asked to write down each day when they fell asleep and when they woke up for 14 straight days. Even then, only 70% of their patients were able to predict their "fall asleep time" within 30 minutes of their actual sleep time.

So, the reality is that most people cannot predict very accurately when they might fall asleep. So how do you know, if you take some potion, that you fell asleep 10 minutes faster? You don't. Sleep latency cannot be measured with that degree of certainty, accuracy, or predictability. It is entirely dependent on when the individual claims to normally fall asleep (and when the lights are turned out) and that is simply too erratic and unpredictable. When a technician "turns off" the lights, is not an objective, biological starting point.

Sleep latency is simply an artificial construct used by sleep medicine to obtain some idea of how long it takes patients to fall asleep once they are in a dark room. However, the sleep products industry took the concept and used sleep latency as if it was an entirely objective measurement. It is not. There is no objective beginning. Using sleep latency in this way is as valid as the lie detector.

Both contain an objective as well as a subjective component. For lie detectors the objective measurements are respiration, sweating, heart rate, etc. and the subjective component is a guess at whether the objective findings amount to lying. With sleep latency the objective component is when the person actually falls asleep and the subjective component is guessing when they are beginning to fall asleep. Both concepts have received wide recognition in our society, however, both should be considered science-ish.

INCONVENIENT SLEEP

CHAPTER 4

Buyer B-wear

Athletes and sports teams are always looking for an "edge". They want to win and are often willing to experiment with new equipment, nutrition, strength and conditioning techniques, analytics and just about anything they perceive will help them win. Sleep is an area that athletes and teams are looking to understand and to improve to give them that edge.

Sleep, like many of the new exploratory areas, is much more complex than is generally understood in the sporting world. As a result, athletes and teams have turned to what is easily available – the ubiquitous consumer gadgets that purport to assist with sleep.

This chapter exposes the traps for athletes and teams in falling for such gadgets.

I intend to live forever. So far, so good.

Steven Wright

Wearables, particularly sports wearables, have become ubiquitous in our society. They track, or purport to track, steps, distance travelled, floors climbed, calories burned, active minutes, specific activities or exercises, sleep time, sleep quality and sleep stages, heart rate, fitness scores, workout routes and pace, amongst other things. While these wearables appear new some of them have been around for a long time.

A wearable to measure steps is not new. A Swiss watchmaker, Abraham-Louis Perrelet is widely credited with inventing the first working pedometer in 1780. It was able to count distance travelled and steps taken. Thomas Jefferson, the third President of the United States, Founding Father and author of the Declaration of Independence, was an avid walker. He introduced a pedometer to the United States that he had obtained in France and modestly renamed it the "Tomish meter". "It consisted of weighted metal balls inside a device that swung on a pendulum. It was worn hooked to the belt and with walking hip motion worked on the mechanical process of the swinging of a pendulum." Pretty advanced for the time.

However, the pedometer did not become popular until the 1930s and even then, the popularity was restricted to long distance walkers. Eventually the pedometer underwent several changes and technological advances. Today it is incorporated into almost all fitness trackers and smartphones.

A heart rate monitor that could detect and record continuous heart rates, away from a hospital setting, was under development in the 1950s and went into commercial production in the 1960s. It was developed by American biophysicist, Norman Holter. His monitor was one of the first wearables available to the medical community and is still widely used today.

In the early 1970s Daniel Kripke, an American sleep researcher, was interested in studying patient activity outside his sleep laboratory. After consulting with many colleagues, he and his team built the first wrist actigraph (sleep watch) in 1973. Kripke and his team continued to improve and test their actigraph as technology evolved. The sleep watch is now over 40 years old.

However, not all wearables are necessarily concerned with sleep, heart rate, or even steps taken. One popular product does not measure anything. It simply gives the wearer special powers to improve athletic performance.

Power Balance

In 2006, Josh Rodarmel and his brother Troy had an idea that could revolutionize athletic performance. A silicon wristband fitted with a mylar hologram that could instantly improve strength, balance, and flexibility. They initially tested the product with college athletes and received rave reviews. It was a big hit – the beginning of an athletic wearable revolution. They claimed that the embedded hologram would react with the body's natural energy field to improve balance, strength, and flexibility in any athlete.

The company also wanted to prove to the wearer that it worked as advertised, that the benefits were not an illusion. Their motto became, "NO PROMISES, JUST RESULTS". So, they created physical tests for individuals to take, under the guidance of a salesperson, that would prove to the wearer that the product visibly improved balance, strength, and flexibility. Their customers were impressed.

While the company was able to "wow" individuals they needed to reach a larger audience. They recruited top-level athletes as paid endorsers of their products, including NBA stars Shaquille O'Neal, Derrick Rose, Lamar Odom, and Brandon Jennings.

The product soon took off. Hundreds of other top athletes started wearing the Power Balance wristband including LeBron James, Drew Brees, and stars from every sport including World Series of Poker Champion, Joe Cada, and even famous NFL coach Pete Carroll. The list goes on and on. They were selling millions of the wristbands. The product went international, it was a star.

In December 2010, the Power Balance wristband was named "Sports Product of the Year" by *CNBC*. Months later the company purchased the naming rights to the home of the Sacramento Kings of the NBA. The "Power Balance Pavilion" was born.

Power Balance also had a friend in the National Hockey League. At the end of the regular season in 2009–10 the Philadelphia Flyers had just squeaked into the playoffs earning the 7th seed out of 8 playoff teams in the East Coast Conference. They had not made the Stanley Cup finals in 12 years and they were in a tough conference.

At the beginning of the playoffs the team's then strength and conditioning coach, Jim McCrossin, purchased Power Balance bands for the whole team of 23+ players. The Flyers went on to defeat the New Jersey Devils, the second seed, 4 games to 1.

Next they faced the number 6 seed, the Boston Bruins. The series went to 7 games, but the Flyers eventually prevailed. They then defeated the Montreal Canadians 4 games to 1 in the East Coast Conference Championship and headed to the Stanley Cup finals. They ended up losing to the Chicago Blackhawks in the Stanley Cup final, 4 games to 2. Still, quite an accomplishment for a team that barely made the playoffs. At the end of the playoffs McCrossin said that just over half the players were still wearing the bands, the other half felt it didn't make a difference.

Later that year, *CNBC* acknowledged that the Power Balance company was having some growing pains:

> Power Balance was recently chastised by the Australian government and fined by Italian and Spanish governments over claims which the company no longer makes. In Spain, where the Department of Health estimated Power Balance sold 300,000 bracelets in the country worth approximately $13 million, they fined the company about $20,000. Italian authorities fined Power Balance approximately $463,000 for deceptive marketing. The company's Italian distributor was also fined about $66,000.

Power Balance responded,

> 'The issues in Australia, Italy and Spain are in regards to previous marketing and advertising messages that we are working to correct, while also offering dissatisfied customers a full refund.' Rodarmel said. 'We believe in Power Balance, as do athletes across the world.'

The "issues" in Australia involved the Australian Competition and Consumer Commission which had determined that the marketing and advertising of Power Balance had broken the law. Power Balance had to change their advertisements and they issued the following statement:

> In our advertising we stated that Power Balance wristbands improved your strength, balance and flexibility.
>
> We admit that there is no credible scientific evidence that supports our claims and therefore we engaged in misleading conduct in breach of s52 of the Trade Practices Act 1974.
>
> If you feel you have been misled by our promotions, we wish to unreservedly apologise and offer a full refund.

The wheels were beginning to come off. On January 4, 2011, the California law firm of Panish Shea & Boyle LLP filed a nationwide class action lawsuit against Power Balance LLC and its owners. They alleged that Power Balance LLC had violated various sections of the California Business & Professions Code. The lawsuit settled for about $57 million dollars.

On March 1, 2011, researchers from the Department of Exercise and Sport Science at the University of Wisconsin published their research on the Power Balance claims. They tested 42 athletes using the same tests promoted by the company. They found that on the first tests of flexibility, balance and strength there was no difference between those wearing the bracelet and those wearing a placebo. When the tests were repeated for a second time there was significant improvement in performance, but no difference between those that wore the bracelet and those that wore a placebo. The researchers concluded that the improvements, while real, were all due to learning the task and had nothing to do with the Power Balance bracelet.

On November 18, 2011, Power Balance LLC filed for Chapter 11 Bankruptcy. That's an American legal process that generally allows a business to continue operating while attempting to restructure its debts. They claimed assets of $1– $10 million dollars and debts between $10 and $50 million dollars. The list of creditors included the Los Angeles Kings National Hockey League team and the Sacramento Kings National Basketball Association team.

Undeterred, Power Balance LLP issued a statement saying they had been the target of numerous class action lawsuits and although the accusations were "baseless" they had cost the company millions of dollars in legal fees.

In November 2012, despite the class action lawsuit, the research debunking their claims, and Power Balance's own admissions that there was no scientific basis for their claims, the NBA partnered with Power Balance to incorporate team logos onto the bracelets and distribute them to the teams.

Mark Cuban, owner of the NBA's Dallas Mavericks, and television star on the program *Shark Tank*, was not a fan of the product. "It was a scam when they were on '*Shark Tank*.' It's still a scam. I don't care if the NBA was dumb enough to sign an agreement; this is going where it belongs." He dumped a Power Balance display case into a garbage can and refused to let his players wear the bracelets.

Today the Power Balance bracelet is still being made and sold. They say that it is worn by millions of consumers and athletes worldwide and that it is now based on Eastern philosophies. The company makes no claims as to any benefits from the bracelet, relying instead on the consumer to decide based on their own experience. Ironically, Power Balance became concerned with fake Power Balance bracelets in the marketplace. They even have a section on their website for customers to report such fakes.

While products like the Power Balance band would seem to demonstrate the gullibility of some athletes (and we are all athletes, to some degree) it also speaks to their desire to improve their performance and gain an edge, no matter what.

Actigraphs or Sleep Watches

Daniel Kripke majored in English literature at Harvard University and obtained a medical degree from Columbia University in Psychiatry in 1965. During his medical studies Kripke became interested in sleep. The summer after his first year of medical school he travelled to the University of California San Francisco to work on sleep research using polysomnography and was hooked. But after graduating from medical school during the Vietnam War he was drafted into the military and assigned to the 6571st Aeromedical Research Laboratory at Holloman Air Force Base in New Mexico.

There he became interested, not only in the data from the polysomnography machine, but also in what else was going on with the patient outside the laboratory. In 1971, Kripke moved to the University of California San Diego as an assistant professor where he was asked to set up a polysomnography sleep lab. He also began experiments with a device to measure motion on the wrist as he wanted to study the circadian rhythms of patients with mania and depression outside the laboratory by measuring their movements 24/7. He co-created the first algorithm that converts motion data from the wrist into sleep data. It's called the Cole-Kripke algorithm and is still used in the sleep watch industry.

Much of the research money to develop the first sleep watch came from the U.S. Government Small Business Innovation Research (SBIR) funding. It took time to develop a sleep watch that actually worked.

Kripke and his team never obtained patents for their work. In an interview Kripke stated, "I am glad I didn't, because the field wasn't ready 25 years ago and I would have wasted a lot of effort." Their valuable software was all open source.

There were several other people involved in the development of this new technology. Bill Gruen, not exactly a household name, went on to develop and commercialize the modern medical-grade actigraph. Born in Vienna the year after World War I ended, he graduated with a technology degree in 1938 at the age of 19. That year Austria was annexed by the German Third Reich and Gruen emigrated to the United States and served in the U.S. Army.

After his military service he went to school to study electronics. In 1957 he graduated from the Institute of Radio Engineers and in 1976 obtained an M.A. from New York University. He worked on and developed a number of medical monitoring products and founded a New York firm, Ambulatory Monitoring, in the 1970s that designed and sold actigraphs for sleep research. He was a Fellow of the New York Academy of Sciences and a board member of the National Sleep Foundation and had numerous contacts throughout the science world. His actigraph, the "Motionlogger", became the go-to product for sleep researchers and is still in use today. His contributions made sleep research outside laboratories possible and more accessible to the research and medical communities.

In 1991 there were only a handful of published research papers focusing on sleep and actigraphy. In 2009, 400 papers were published on sleep and actigraphy.

In 1995, the American Academy of Sleep Medicine (AASM) reviewed the published literature on actigraphy and provided guidance to physicians on when and how actigraphy might be helpful. Further reviews were undertaken in 2003 and 2007. It was the 2007 review that opened the door for greater use of actigraphy in the diagnosis and treatment of sleep disorders. The AASM said:

> Actigraphy provides an acceptably accurate estimate of sleep patterns in normal, healthy adult populations and in [] patients suspected of certain sleep disorders.

By 2008, actigraphy had transitioned from being an emerging technology to an accepted method for determining if a person was awake or asleep, usually with at least 90% accuracy. However, such actigraphs had to be validated against polysomnography and be U.S. Food and Drug Administration cleared. Further, doctors and researchers had to review and interpret the data, not the patients. Individuals who were interested in measuring their own sleep did not normally have access to the technology as it was expensive, and the data was difficult to interpret.

That all changed after 2009 with the explosion of consumer-grade sleep watches. Products like Fitbit and Basis gave the consumer the opportunity to measure their own sleep without the cost and complicated data associated with medical-grade sleep watches. However, the medical community was not impressed with what they were seeing from these new consumer products.

In 2018, the AASM published a report saying that consumer-grade actigraphs should not be used to diagnose or treat patients. They said:

> Rather than being sold as medical devices or apps, most CSTs [consumer sleep technology] are self-described "lifestyle/entertainment" devices that are not subject to United States Food and Drug Administration (FDA) oversight. ... The lack of validation data and absence of FDA clearance raises concerns about the accuracy of CST data. The CST-generated data is not standardized, and raw data and proprietary algorithms are typically unavailable to clinicians.

Daniel Kripke, the inventor of actigraphy, reflected on the technology he created:

> I am very gratified that wrist actigraphy is being used very widely in sleep research, which was my intention, because I realized very early that polysomnography was too cumbersome for the length and quantity of recordings that were needed for many studies.
>
> ...
>
> Also, I have now 25 years experience with using actigraphs for clinical purposes, and I am chagrined that none of the commercial software I have seen (Fitbit, Basis, and Microsoft) is of any use at all for clinical purposes. I understand that the companies do not want to bother earning FDA approval as medical devices and are happy making money with what they are doing, but the sleep data they provide is not much more informative than a fortune cookie.

...

> The doctors at our Scripps Sleep Clinic complain that patients bring in all different sorts of data from their wrist monitors, and the doctors can't make head nor tail out of it. They are correct. Most of it is nonsense, and the useful information isn't formatted in useful form.

In March 2016, a group of academic sports scientists and engineers from Germany, Sweden, Norway, and Australia headed by Peter Düking published a review of wearables for athletes. They looked at a wide variety of technologies and the science behind them, including such things as heart rate monitors, sleep monitors, GPS, etc. They concluded that,

> Most of the wearables currently available have not yet been evaluated scientifically, even though evaluation of their reliability, validity and accuracy at the very least, particularly in connection with training, is critical for athletes to be able to use them with confidence.

Nevertheless, consumer-grade actigraphs hit the market in 2009 and their use has exploded. They come in all kinds of shapes, sizes, and colours. The manufacturers market products that purport to measure sleep with sensors on your wrist, on your finger, on your head, in your bed and even in your pajamas.

Actigraphs work on the premise that if you are awake your wrists are moving and if your wrists are not moving, you are asleep. Of course, it is not quite that simple.

One very important thing to remember is: sleep is a complicated process that takes place in your brain and your brain is not on your wrist or finger!

On the Wrist

In 2006, Nintendo released its unique Wii system. The remote control or wand contained accelerometers and made gaming more fun and interactive. You could control an on-screen avatar with just body movements. It was a fun game and a huge hit. James Park and Eric Friedman couldn't wait to try out the product. They even waited outside Best Buy at 6 am to get one. It also gave them an idea. Why couldn't they create a sports product that was not only fun and interactive, but could provide feedback to the user and encourage them to be more active?

In March of 2007 they incorporated a company, Healthy Metrics Research, Inc. By October they had renamed the company Fitbit, Inc. based out of San Francisco. The device was introduced in 2008 and won second place at the TechCrunch50 Conference that year (although it was not widely available until 2009). The product was called the Fitbit Tracker. It was designed to get people inspired to exercise and sleep well by tracking steps and sleep and providing direct feedback to the user. It was a combination of an actigraph and a pedometer and became a big hit.

Pedometers had been around for a few hundred years, but the information had never been formatted in terms of lifestyle factors. The new Fitbit Tracker could count the number of steps you took and then calculate how many calories you had burned. It could also measure sleep duration. It allowed the user to set goals and to monitor their success. This provided a fun factor and motivation to improve performance.

Fitbit filled a vacuum created by the technology revolution and the desire of individuals to measure and track their own health and fitness. However, with respect to sleep, Fitbit had not undergone testing comparing their tracker to PSG. Fitbit was marketed as a consumer gadget designed to inspire people to be healthy and fit and not as a medical device. However, for many users, sleep was a major concern. They not only wanted their sleep tested, but they wanted solutions to their sleep problems. The Center for Disease Control in the U.S. estimated that about 1 in 3 adults in America aren't sleeping enough. It was becoming an epidemic and people wanted solutions.

On May 8, 2015, a class action lawsuit was filed against Fitbit, by James Brickman. The complaint alleged, among other things, that Fitbits could not accurately measure sleep or sleep quality. They argued that Fitbit advertising misled consumers and that (amongst other things), "The Fitbit sleep-tracking function consistently overestimated sleep by *67 minutes per night* as compared to what the polysomnography reported." The Fitbit sleep tracker class action settlement was granted approval on March 20, 2020. That settlement was appealed on April 20, 2020. The results are pending.

Fitbit began to grow and innovate their products. From 2010 to 2015 their revenue increased from 5 million to about 1.8 billion dollars. In 2015, they launched an IPO at a valuation of 3.4 billion dollars. The largest ever IPO valuation for a wearable at that time. In the first 9 months of 2016 they sold 15.8 million devices.

Given the open source software developed by Kripke and his colleagues and the reduced price of accelerometers, Fitbit soon attracted multiple competitors. Early on, newer sleep watches largely competed on price, colour, wearability, battery life, data reporting and customer experience. Some competitors focused on providing unique data for a particular sport such as running or swimming, by adding GPS and additional waterproofing. However, in terms of sleep there was not much advantage to be gained. Attempts at squeezing more information about sleep out of wrist motion sensors was fruitless, all that could really be measured was whether the wearer was awake or asleep, nothing more.

A 2012 study of 24 healthy adults by researchers at West Virginia University concluded, "Fitbit has the same specificity limitations as actigraphy; both devices consistently misidentify wake as sleep and thus overestimate both sleep time and quality."

On the Finger

Some wearers of actigraphs complain that they do not like to wear a watch to bed. They find it inconvenient or uncomfortable and, in some cases, think it simply keeps them awake at night. Oura Health Ltd. had a better idea. Founded in Finland in 2013, the company decided to miniaturize actigraphy technology, add sensors to measure body temperature and heart rate, and put it all into a finger ring. It became an easy-to-wear stylish ring.

Oura Health Ltd. says that their sensors can determine, like actigraphy, when a person is awake and when they are asleep and can therefore determine total sleep time as well as how long it takes to fall asleep. They also claim that the ring can determine your sleep stages (light, deep and REM). They point to two studies, one conducted by their company and one by SRI International, an independent California research agency.

The aim of Oura's own 2016 research, "was to validate the

OURA ring in its ability to detect the amount of sleep and sleep quality against the gold standard sleep laboratory test." Fourteen subjects wore OURA rings while undergoing additional sleep testing. Eight of the subjects used a home brain wave (EEG test) and six used a home test that only measured eye movements. The results failed to validate the product. In any event, at-home EEG and eye movement tests are not a standard way to validate sleep monitors.

The 2018 SRI study was a bit more comprehensive and helpful. SRI studied the sleep of 41 healthy adolescents and young adults. They were also careful to screen the subjects to ensure they did not suffer from any condition, including mental health issues, that might affect their sleep. The subjects each wore an OURA ring while undergoing an overnight PSG study.

SRI found that the OURA ring was (mostly) within 30 minutes of recorded total sleep time compared to PSG. Not surprisingly, the company relies on this report in their marketing. However, the SRI study was unable to say that the ring could determine sleep stages. They said the ring underestimated deep sleep by 20 minutes and overestimated REM sleep by 17 minutes. They went on to say that the ring had "potential" but that more, "future development and validation is needed." In terms of accuracy, it seems that measuring sleep with a finger ring is not much different than measuring sleep with a wrist actigraph.

In Your Pajamas

In 2019, researchers at the University of Massachusetts unveiled their "smart pajamas" or "Phyjamas" as they call them. They developed a method of implanting sensors into pajamas that they say can measure heart rate, breathing and sleep posture. You, of course, would have to wear *their* Phyjamas. Their assumption is that if you know how you sleep and in what position(s) you can learn more about your sleep and how to improve it. Nice theory, except there is virtually no research that shows sleeping position(s) have much of an effect on healthy adults' sleep duration or quality. That, and you would have to wear the same pajamas every night!

In Bed Sensors and Apps

There are numerous apps and in-bed sensors that do not require the user to wear anything. Just place the sensors in your bed or put your phone beside the bed and when you wake up you will get information on your sleep. Some claim to measure how long and how well you sleep, others claim to be able to detect your sleep stages. As the AASM points out, most lack proper validation.

However, despite the lack of validation data, most consumer sleep technology can measure whether a person is awake or whether they are asleep, just not always with the same accuracy as medical-grade actigraphs or PSG. Kathryn Russo and her colleagues at the Department of Neurology at the Massachusetts General Hospital raised an important point, "The common implication across the marketing of consumer sleep monitors is that tracking sleep will lead to improved sleep." That seems to be the hope anyways.

Sleep watches are not much different than a bathroom scale. You can stand on a bathroom scale and it will tell you how much you weigh, but nothing else. If it says you weigh 180 lbs. what does that mean? Is it good or bad? If you are 5 feet tall you would be considered obese. If you are 6 feet tall your weight would be normal. Is 180 lbs. your normal weight? Have you gained or lost weight? A single number like your weight (or your sleep hours) must be individualized and put into context.

A bathroom scale is a way to keep score, it is a point in time. A bathroom scale cannot tell you why you may be underweight or overweight. Individuals need to consult with a doctor to determine if they have an issue with their weight, what may have caused any issue and what can be done about it. They need a diagnosis and a plan and maybe help in losing or gaining weight. The bathroom scale doesn't do that for you. Measuring sleep with a sleep watch, even if it is reasonably accurate, is no different. Tracking sleep to improve sleep is as useful as measuring your weight to lose weight. Both require much more to be successful.

There are consumer sleep products that not only measure sleep duration and timing, but also provide some sleep coaching to improve sleep hygiene. While it may be helpful to some consumers that approach often ignores the multiple causes of poor sleep including sleep disorders, mental health issues, organic diseases, injuries, etc.

Dream On

Not all consumer sleep products purport to just measure sleep, one product claims to actually improve your sleep. Dreem is unique amongst consumer wearables. It is a headband that is worn at night and designed to measure EEG brainwaves, heart rate, breathing rate, and head movement. The Dreem company, in their 2019 Whitepaper, claims that the information collected can tell when you sleep, how long you sleep, how often you wake up, your heart rate, breathing rate, and what sleep stages you are in (light sleep, deep sleep and REM sleep).

In order to "improve" your sleep the headband tracks your brain waves and when you enter a deep sleep the device produces a sound that causes the height or amplitude of the brain wave to increase. (The noise that is used is called "pink noise" and is very much like steady rain, wind, rustling leaves, or even heartbeats. The sound is flat.)

Their theory is that by exposing a person to pink noise at the right time it can increase their deep sleep or at least the height of their deep sleep brainwave. However, they don't say how increasing the amplitude is helpful to a person's overall sleep or performance or how that might affect other sleep stages. Artificially manipulating sleep stages seems perilous.

The company says that their headband also contains a "smart alarm". The theory behind smart alarms is that you should ideally wake up during light sleep rather than in a deep sleep. If you wake up from a deep sleep, you will experience sleep inertia. That is the feeling of grogginess and disorientation that can affect your reaction time and ability to pay attention for 15 – 30 minutes, after waking up. There is no indication that waking up while in a deep sleep has any other affects beyond the typical 15 – 30 minute "groggy" window. Dreem says that they can tell when you are in a light sleep and wake you up with an alarm, thus avoiding the short "groggy" period.

It is not unusual for a consumer sleep product to be brought to market without proper validation studies to support their claims. They are, after all, not medical devices and therefore do not require validation by regulators.

Many of the new consumer sleep trackers are also trying to measure sleep stages. You can wake up in the morning and see how much light sleep, deep sleep and REM sleep you had during the night.

Sounds interesting.

The problem of course is that the brain decides what sleep stages it needs and when. There is no "normal" amount of time to spend in each sleep stage. Some research suggests that it is normal to spend 50 - 60% of your time in light sleep, 10 – 25% of your time in deep sleep and 20 – 25% of your time in REM sleep. A pretty wide range of "normal".

Doctors at Harvard Medical School say that sleep patterns are affected by multiple factors including age, time of day and other behaviours prior to sleep. Additionally, they say:

> Sleep history – the quantity and quality of an individual's sleep in recent days – can also have dramatic effects on sleep patterns. Repeatedly missing a night's sleep, an irregular sleep schedule, or frequent disturbance of sleep can result in a redistribution of sleep stages.

More importantly, even if the consumer devices could accurately measure sleep stages what would you do with the information? It is not sufficient to diagnose sleep disorders and you cannot go to bed at night hoping to get more deep sleep or any other stage of sleep. You cannot consciously control that function. Why measure something you cannot do anything about?

Athletes are not really interested in the "entertainment" value of sleep monitoring offered by consumer gadgets. They want to improve their sleep and their performance. They expect results.

Sleep science and the science of wearables is not taught to most trainers, sport scientists and team physicians. They often have to rely on the manufacturers of the products to train them. Teams and athletes can make important decisions that can affect athlete travel, health, fitness, readiness, and recovery based on the results from wearables. It is difficult for them to figure out what works and what doesn't work. They are also not helped by popular culture and the media. In 2005 *Time Magazine* listed a consumer sleep monitor amongst its "inventions of the year". The product had no published validation studies.

Athletes and sports teams need to ask hard questions about the validity, reliability and claims of any product they are thinking of using. Particularly in a new and evolving field such as sleep. It is really just asking, "what problem am I trying to solve?", and "what tool helps me solve that problem?"

CHAPTER 5

The Research-ish Theory

To most of the public, including many athletes, "science" is often considered to have all or at least most of the answers to hard questions. Science is often considered to have a great deal of credibility and it is not unusual to see the term "proven by science" to support some product or idea.

However, real science can be somewhere between a credible concept and a wild west show. Science is about ideas but can be influenced by personalities and sometimes greed. This chapter explores those issues and hopefully assists readers in understanding what it means when something is "proven by science".

There are three kinds of lies: lies, damn lies and statistics.

Benjamin Disraeli

For the most part, scientists have always communicated the results of their experiments by publishing articles in scientific journals. The first such journal, Le Journal des Scavans (Journal of the Learned), was published in 1665, over 350 years ago, in France. It consisted of 12 pages. At that time the stated goal of the journal was to provide information on all the new scientific findings, "there is nothing that occurs in Europe worth be known by men of letters that you cannot learn from this Journal". It contained a list of new books, obituaries of famous people, and "experiments and discoveries in physics and chemistry." It also contained some non-scientific information such as decisions from religious and secular courts and edicts of censorship concerning science. Aside from a period of time during the French Revolution, that journal has been in continuous publication since its inception. Although, in modern times it has become more concerned with the arts rather than science.

As science and the number of scientists has expanded over the millennia so has the number of scientific publications. So much so that, thanks to the internet and online publications, no one actually knows how many scientific publications there are in existence today, let alone how many individual scientific papers have been published. Some estimate that there are over 23,000 peer-reviewed scientific journals; others say that there are more than 28,000 peer-reviewed journals not including the many fake journals out there. Researchers at the University of Ottawa in Canada estimate that over 50 million science articles had already been published by 2009, with an estimated 1.5 million new articles published each year. That is hardly surprising since there are currently about 8 million scientists worldwide. Further, about 90% of all scientists who ever existed, are alive today, and they are publishing up a storm. If the University of Ottawa is correct then there are 285 new scientific articles published every hour, 24 hours a day, 7 days a week, all year long, year after year. Who has time to read that many articles? (Or who wants to?)

What has changed over the years is the importance of published scientific papers. Scientific publications are much more than a way for scientists to communicate knowledge; they have become the "currency" of science. Scientists and institutions measure their success by the volume of publications they produce. For scientists wanting to achieve tenure at a university it is "publish or perish". The process and drive to obtain funding and to publish research can lead to some difficulties.

Scientists like to publish unique, novel papers that attract the public's attention. Of course, that can also drive future funding for their research. In order to satisfy that demand and to enhance their own careers some scientists focus on headline-grabbing research. Others prefer to "pad" their CV with large numbers of publications. This is sometimes called the salami effect. A scientist could publish his/her findings in one paper but prefers to chop it up and publish a handful of papers instead. The goal for many is the volume of publications not necessarily the quality.

Scientists are also human beings and subject to the same frailties as other people. Some simply cheat or fudge their results to grab headlines and secure funding for more research and their employment.

The Miracle Discovery

Stem cells are a bit like blank slates. They are "empty" cells within our bodies that can morph into specialized cells allowing certain parts of our bodies to repair themselves. For example, there are stem cells in the brain, bone marrow, and liver that allow each of those parts to regenerate any damage or wear and tear.

Millions of people die each year due to heart damage from heart attacks. If the damaged heart cells could regenerate from stem cells, millions of lives could be saved each year. However, it has long been recognized that the human heart does not contain stem cells that allow it to regenerate or grow new heart muscle.

However, all of that seemed to change in 2000. At a meeting of the American Heart Association, Piero Anversa, a professor at New York Medical College, walked up to the podium and told the audience about the results of his new experiments. What he told them shocked the scientific community and made Anversa a scientific rock star.

He had injected bone marrow stem cells into the hearts of mice and they were able to successfully regenerate heart muscle. A potential miracle cure for humans. He and his colleagues published their findings in 2001 in *Nature*. His research went viral. It was the talk of the scientific community. Companies even began injecting bone marrow into peoples' damaged hearts in the hope these new cells would repair their hearts.

However, not everyone was convinced. There was a lot of head scratching amongst medical researchers. At the 2000 meeting of the American Heart Association two researchers from Indiana University School of Medicine were in attendance. They had tried the same experiment in the late 1990s (a few years earlier) but could not find any new heart cells in the mice. They never published their negative findings. But, after listening to Anversa they decided to go back to their lab and try again. They again failed to find any new heart cells. What had they missed? This time they published their negative findings in *Nature* in 2004. Other scientists from Stanford University and the University of Bonn were also unable to replicate Anversa's experiments. No one else could find these new heart cells. Questions were raised. However, Anversa's team dismissed the negative findings of the other scientists. Their research required special techniques. Other scientists simply did not know how to conduct the experiments properly.

Despite doubts in the scientific community about whether the heart could regenerate from bone marrow stem cells Anversa was given a great honour. In 2007 he was awarded a full professorship at Harvard Medical School and a director position at Brigham and Women's Hospital's Center for Regenerative Medicine. Anversa and his team had established themselves as leaders in the field and continued to conduct research and publish their findings. This time with the backing of two prestigious institutions.

Anversa's team looked at new ways to prove that heart muscles could indeed regenerate. In the 1950s people were exposed to a great deal of radiation largely from nuclear testing. The radioactive isotopes persisted throughout their bodies as they aged, except in organs that could regenerate. In those organs, new cells would replace the old ones containing radioactive isotopes. Thus if an organ can regenerate cells then the amount of radiation should be lower.

One of Anversa's colleagues Jan Kajstura thought that if the radiation levels in the hearts of older people (who had earlier radiation exposure) turned out to be the same as the radiation levels in younger people (with much less radiation exposure) then that would be proof the heart could regenerate.

Jan Kajstura worked with Bruce Buchholz, a scientist at the Lawrence Livermore National Laboratory, to conduct the experiments as that institution had the necessary radiation data. In 2012, Kajstura published his results. Indeed, the hearts of older people had the same amount of radiation as younger people. It was proof that the heart could regenerate. The old cells with radioactive isotopes were being replaced by new heart cells. But when Buchholz read the paper, he was shocked. That was not the data he had provided. Kajstura had altered the data to fit his theory. Buchholz recognized the fraud and was furious. He confronted Anversa's team. The wheels were starting to come off and Harvard University was paying attention.

In January 2013, investigators from Harvard Medical School and Brigham and Women's Hospital raided Anversa's laboratory seizing notes and computers. Anversa hired lawyers and blamed Kajstura for any misconduct. Kajstura left Harvard that same year. Doubts in the scientific community persisted as other researchers still could not replicate Anversa's experiments.

In 2015, Anversa, the scientific rock star, was dismissed from Harvard. The Brigham and Women's Hospital and some affiliates agreed to pay $10 million dollars to the Department of Justice to settle allegations that Anversa, Kajstura, and another colleague, "knew, or should have known, that their work included, 'improper protocols, invalid and inaccurately characterized cardiac stem cells, reckless or deliberately misleading record-keeping, and discrepancies and/or fabrications of data and images.'" It had all been fake.

In 2018, *The New York Times* detailed the entire controversy of Anversa's work. The final report from Harvard determined that he "committed research misconduct" but the evidence did not support that he was responsible for the "malfeasance". Harvard did not name the culprits. They did, however, request that 31 of his scientific papers published in respected journals over the span of a decade be retracted. *The New York Times* summed up the case:

> Dr. Anversa's story has laid bare some of the hazards of modern medical research: the temptation to embrace a promising new theory, the reluctance to heed contrary evidence and the institutional barriers to promptly stopping malfeasance.

Anversa had been wrong; heart cells could not regenerate. However, his theory had persisted for over a decade and even spawned new medical treatments. There are people walking around today who have had bone marrow stem cells injected into their heart, a completely useless treatment.

The Sleep Connection

Sleep research is not immune. Robert Fogel, an Assistant Professor of Medicine and Associate Physician at Harvard Medical School and a Co-Director of the Fellowship in Sleep Medicine at Brigham and Women's Hospital, admitted that he had falsified sleep research data in a published paper. The Office of Research Integrity at the National Institutes of Health noted that his study of sleep apnea in severely obese patients, published in the journal *Sleep* in 2003 was fake. The journal later retracted the article.

Specifically, Fogel was found to have done the following in the paper:

- Changed/falsified roughly half the physiologic data
- Fabricated roughly 20% of the anatomic data that were supposedly obtained from Computed Tomography (CT) images
- Changed/falsified 50 to 80 percent of the other anatomic data
- Changed/falsified roughly 40 to 50 percent of the sleep data so that those data would better conform to his hypothesis.

How did he get caught? He confessed to his former mentor. There were apparently no mechanisms in place to detect such faked research. Fogel's punishment? He signed a voluntary settlement agreement where he promised to "exclude himself from serving in any advisory capacity to" the U.S. Public Health Service for three years. In addition, if any institution is given Public Health Service grants for research involving Fogel during those three years, it must submit a plan of supervision and certify that any data produced by Fogel was, "based on actual experiments". The three years were up March 16, 2012.

Tip of the Iceberg

The prevailing view in the scientific community is that such fraud is relatively rare and likely limited to a "few bad apples". Others disagree. Daniele Fanelli, at the University of Edinburgh, argues that such fraud may very well be the, "tip of the iceberg". In 2009 he published a meta-analysis of 18 surveys looking at the frequency with which scientists fabricate and falsify data. His conclusions were shocking. He noted that confirmed cases of published fraud amongst scientists is widely considered to be 1 – 2% of all research. However, when scientists, particularly those in the biomedical field are asked about their and their colleagues' involvement in misconduct the answers are quite different. Fanelli wrote:

> This is the first meta-analysis of surveys asking scientists about their experiences of misconduct. It found that, on average, about 2% of scientists admitted to have fabricated, falsified or modified data or results at least once – a serious form of misconduct my (sic) any standard – and up to one third admitted a variety of other questionable research practices including "dropping data points based on a gut feeling", and "changing the design, methodology or results of a study in response to pressures from a funding source". In surveys asking about the behaviour of colleagues, fabrication, falsification and modification had been observed, on average, by over 14% of respondents, and other questionable practices by up to 72%.

Fanelli considers the estimates from his meta-analysis to be "conservative".

Of course, most scientists bristle at the notion that their work is less than credible. However, there are some systemic issues that have crept into scientific publications. Over the years scientists (and publishers) have been more and more reluctant to publish negative results. From 1990 until 2013 papers describing "negative results" dropped from an overall rate of 30% to just 14% of published papers. There are many reasons why scientists and publishers are reluctant to publish negative results, but failing to do so can have adverse effects on scientific knowledge. For example, if the two scientists from the Indiana University School of Medicine had published their negative findings in the 1990s on bone marrow stem cells and heart muscle regeneration that might have created a much more lively and critical debate about Anversa's early claims and prevented a decade of fraud. Also, if negative results are not published then the results of meta-analysis can be skewed. It could create the illusion that there is a positive association between two factors when there may not be any positive association at all.

Preventing outright fraud is difficult and requires institutions to implement strict oversight through policies, procedures, and enforcement. Of course, there are other mistakes and errors that do not necessarily involve fraud but can be equally problematic. Sometimes science and statistics can simply become overly complicated. Many, but certainly not all, journals use a "peer-review" system to overcome the problem. They send out papers they are about to publish to numerous scientists familiar with the field and solicit feedback. They often forward any objections to the author to address. Sometimes this can result in modifications to the original paper or even a withdrawal of the paper if the errors are serious enough. Sometimes the feedback is ignored. While well intentioned, the peer review system is hardly fool-proof.

In 1998 Fiona Godlee was appointed as Editor of the prestigious British Journal of Medicine (BMJ), the first woman editor in the 160-plus-year history of the journal. She set out to see how their peer review system might be affected if the reviewers did not know the authors' names. She felt perhaps familiarity with the authors might skew the reviewers' responses. She was also curious if the reviews might be affected if they had to sign the reviews, rather than submit them anonymously. It turned out that those two factors had no real effect on peer-review at the BMJ. There were, however, other shocking results.

Godlee took a perfectly good paper that was about to be published, introduced obvious errors and sent it out to 420 BMJ reviewers for comment:

> In total, 8 areas of weakness in design, analysis, or interpretation had been introduced into the manuscript. The mean [average] number of weaknesses commented on was 2. Only 10% of reviewers identified 4 or more areas of weakness, and 16% failed to identify any.

Despite the deficiencies of the manuscript, of those that reviewed the paper: 33% recommended publication with minor revisions, 12% recommended publication with major revisions, 30% recommended the paper be rejected, and 25% made no recommendation concerning publication. It is shocking to see that most peer reviewers at a prestigious publication like the BMJ failed to find most of the errors in the publication under review. Did they not take the time to carefully review the paper, or did they not understand the scientific errors that were introduced? The BMJ did not speculate.

While many major publications take "peer-review" seriously, science has become overly complex, particularly with respect to epidemiology and statistical analysis. In fact, Godlee found that scientists with post-graduate training in those fields tended to comment on the most errors.

While distinguished journals grapple with the concept and process of "peer-review" other journals are not so concerned.

With the proliferation of online journals, many marketed as "peer-reviewed", the problem seems to be getting worse. Many of the "peer-reviewed" online journals merely ask their reviewers if the paper is methodologically sound, a rather shoddy method of "peer-review". Other journals don't even go that far or even attempt "peer-review", despite claiming they do so.

The Completely Fake Paper

John Bohannon earned his PhD in molecular biology from the University of Oxford in 2002. He went on to specialize in bioethics and became a science journalist. While a visiting scholar at the Harvard University Program in Ethics and Health he conducted an interesting experiment that revealed what "peer-reviewed" really meant in the burgeoning open-access science journal business.

He created a fake scientist (Ocorrafoo Cobange) from a fake institution (the Wassee Institute of Medicine) and a fake scientific experiment (which found that an extract from lichens had anticancer properties). Bohannon submitted his fake article to 304 "peer-reviewed" journals. More than half the journals (157) accepted the paper. Anyone who had bothered to even Google his name or the institution would have realized the whole thing was fake. He chronicled his venture in *Science Magazine* in 2013:

> In fact, it should have been promptly rejected. Any reviewer with more than a high-school knowledge of chemistry and the ability to understand a basic data plot should have spotted the paper's shortcomings

immediately. Its experiments are so hopelessly flawed that the results are meaningless.

Bohannon continued:

> Acceptance was the norm, not the exception. The paper was accepted by journals hosted by industry titans Sage and Elsevier. The paper was accepted by journals published by prestigious academic institutions such as Kobe University in Japan. It was accepted by scholarly society journals. It was even accepted by journals for which the paper's topic was utterly inappropriate, such as the Journal of Experimental & Clinical Assisted Reproduction.

Online open-access journals differ from more traditional journals in their business models. Traditional journals charge the consumer to read the research whether that is an institution or an individual. Open-access journals provide the research papers for free but often charge the scientist to publish their work. John Bohannon exposed the lack of meaningful "peer-review" involved with some of the open-access journals. However, he made it clear that the open-access model, by itself, was not necessarily to blame. David Roos, a biologist at the University of Pennsylvania, told him that if he "had targeted traditional, subscription-based journals, … 'I strongly suspect you would get the same results.'" It's just that open-access journals publish many more articles which tends to magnify the problem.

N is a Big Number

Two years later, in 2015, John Bohannon was at it again.

He, along with a few colleagues published a paper in the *International Archives of Medicine* called, "Chocolate with a high Cocoa content as a weight-loss accelerator". He used a pseudonym, Johannes Bohannon (not much of a disguise), and used a fake institute, the Institute of Diet and Health, which existed only as a website. However, everything else was real, including his colleagues, which included a medical doctor and a statistician. They conducted a real clinical trial on chocolate and weight loss.

They recruited subjects from the Frankfurt area via Facebook. They were paid 150 Euros each to participate in the diet study. Subjects were randomly divided into three groups. One group ate a low-carbohydrate diet, another group ate a low-carbohydrate diet but also ate 1.5 oz of dark chocolate each day and a third group made no changes to their current diet (the control group). The experiment was to run for three weeks. Every subject underwent a thorough medical exam, including blood tests and a questionnaire. They weighed themselves every morning. In total, 18 individual metrics were collected including BMI, sleep, a well-being analysis, and blood tests for cholesterol.

After three weeks the data was analyzed. The researchers found that the subjects in the chocolate group had a statistically significant increase in their well-being compared to the low-carb group. In addition, although both low-carb groups (with and without chocolate intake) lost weight in comparison to the control group, the low-carb diet group that ate chocolate lost weight 10% faster, a statistically significant difference. They said that the experiment proved that chocolate was in fact a "weight loss turbo".

They wanted to share the news with the world. The paper was submitted to 20 scientific journals and was accepted by multiple journals within 24 hours. Bohannon chose the *International Archives of Medicine* as the Editor claimed that, "'all articles submitted to the journal are reviewed in a rigorous way'". They paid the 600 Euro fee for publication and the article was published within 2 weeks with not a single change.

The story gets a bit better. Like many researchers with significant findings (and sexy results) they sent out a press release in English and German. It soon made the front page of *Bild*, the best-selling European newspaper, "Those who eat chocolate stay slim!", the headline read. The research made headlines everywhere including places like India, Texas, and Australia. It even appeared in *Shape*, an English-language fitness magazine.

Then John Bohannon stepped up and withdrew the published paper and published a new article, "I Fooled Millions Into Thinking Chocolate Helps Weight Loss. Here's How." He wanted to make the point that some scientific journals would publish anything and that journalists, even those that purport to be reporting about science, would write anything if it had a sexy headline without any real review. Again, a simple Google search would have discovered that Johannes Bohannon and the Institute of Diet and Health were fake. Not even the science reporters did that.

Bohannon did not report the number of subjects in the original article and nobody asked. Not the *International Archives of Medicine* or any reporter. There were only 15 people involved, most of which were women. Five on a low-carb diet, five on a low-carb diet with chocolate and five in the control group. The actual weight loss differences had been trivial. The low-carb group lost 3.1% of their body weight in 21 days, the chocolate group lost 3.2% of their body weight in 21 days and the control group gained 0.7%.

Bohannon knew that if he collected a large number of metrics (18) from a small number of subjects (15) that he would have a 60% chance of finding something that was statistically significant even if the differences were trivial. He explained:

> A woman's weight can fluctuate as much as 5 pounds over the course of her menstrual cycle, far greater than the weight difference between our chocolate and low-carb groups. Which is why you need to use a large number of people, and balance age and gender across treatment groups. (We didn't bother).

> You might as well read tea leaves as try to interpret our results. Chocolate may be a weight loss accelerator, or it could be the opposite. You can't even trust the weight loss that our non-chocolate low-carb group experienced versus control. Who knows what the handful of people in the control group were eating? We didn't even ask them.

Although the research was real and the results were real, Bohannon had engaged in what is called p-hacking (or just fiddling with the statistics). In some circles this may not be considered actual fraud, but it sure is a pretty close cousin. Bohannon didn't change any of the numbers, just how they were analyzed. In simple terms, the way experiments are meant to be conducted is that the scientist starts with a hypothesis, collects the data, crunches the numbers through statistical formulas and arrives at a conclusion. It is generally accepted that if the conclusion has only a 5% likelihood of being due to chance then it is considered statistically significant. That is a p-value (probability-value) of less than 0.05.

There are many different ways to fiddle with the statistics if you don't get the results you want or are expecting. You could drop outlier data and crunch the numbers again until you find a statistically significant result. Or you could simply repeat the experiment until you get the result you want. What Bohannon did was use a small number of subjects and collected a large amount of data on each, knowing something would likely show up as a positive result, even if it was meaningless. He did this of course to make a point – that no one would notice. He was right. Bohannon made an interesting observation:

> Luckily, scientists are getting wise to these problems. Some journals are trying to phase out p value significance testing altogether to nudge scientists into better habits. And almost no one takes studies with fewer than 30 subjects seriously anymore. Editors of reputable journals reject them out of hand before sending them to peer reviewers. But there are plenty of journals that care more about money than reputation.

There are many ways that some scientists have fooled the public. Some have outright faked publications while not undertaking any research. Others, have "fudged" their data or, like Anversa, claimed to find things that did not exist. Some have engaged in p-hacking unconsciously or otherwise. Journals, institutions, peer-reviewers and even the press cannot always catch fraud or mistakes and sometimes don't even try. Readers of scientific papers should look at all articles with a discerning eye, particularly when they are applying the results of the research to athletes.

In research involving sleep and athletes, having less than 30 subjects is the rule not the exception. The number of subjects in those studies is often dictated by economics, timing, the availability of athletes, and their willingness to participate. That doesn't mean that the research is necessarily invalid, but it does mean that the research requires very close scrutiny.

There are at least 50 sports journals published on a regular basis. Unfortunately, most practitioners working with athletes simply do not have time to closely read the research or read it at all. They tend to rely on more simple communication like blogs, infographics, review articles, webinars, and podcasts, etc. Sometimes it is important to read the actual article.

The Most Quoted Article

It has been estimated that over 38 million children and adolescents participate in organized sports in the United States alone. Each year about 9% or 3.5 million of them sustain an injury requiring medical treatment. Matthew Milewski, a children's orthopaedic specialist, wanted to find out the reasons for the number of injuries and what could be done about it. Milewski and some colleagues decided to research the matter. They found a private, combined middle/high school in California where students participated in both school and community sports that had a good way of tracking injuries. They defined an "injury" as "any injury that necessitated a visit to the athletic trainer's room for evaluation and/or treatment."

The school's certified athletic trainers were available at all times during practices and games and recorded all injuries, including those injuries that occurred during participation in community sports which were reported back to them.

Milewski and his colleagues obtained permission from 160 students at the school and their parents to access the medical data and for the students to participate in the study. In the end, 112 students participated. The participants were split about 50/50 male and female and their average age was 15. They were each given an online questionnaire consisting of 10 questions. The question about sleep was quite simple, "(5) During the season how many hours of sleep, on average, do you get per night?"

The researchers accessed 21 months of injury data and then crunched the numbers. They arrived at two simple conclusions. The first is that students in the higher grades (older students) had an increased injury risk. For each additional grade in school the athletes were 1.4 times more likely to have an injury. The researchers said the result should have been expected given the rising physical and mental demands of sports as the athletes get older. Their second conclusion was that athletes who slept, on average, less than 8 hours a night were 1.7 times more likely to have an injury compared with athletes that slept more than 8 hours, on average, per night.

The title of the paper was, "Chronic Lack of Sleep is Associated With Increased Sports Injuries in Adolescent Athletes". That title spread rapidly across the sporting world. It was, and still is, the most cited and quoted paper on the subject. It is quoted in virtually every article on why athletes should get more sleep and is mentioned repeatedly in sports blogs, articles, tweets, infographics, webinars, and presentations to athletes, etc. Most cite the title of the paper and the conclusion that sleeping less than 8 hours increased injury risk by 1.7 times. Some note that the research applies specifically to adolescents, however, there should not be much difference in professional athletes as many of them are still adolescents.

On the face of it, the article appears to support the notion that the longer athletes sleep the less likely they are to get injured. However, the paper doesn't exactly support that notion. The research found that those athletes that slept 5 hours per night had the same (or even slightly) less risk of injury than those that slept 7 hours per night. Further, those that slept 5 hours had a decreased injury risk (about 15%) than athletes that slept 6 hours. In terms of injury risk, they were ranked (from lowest to highest) 9 hours, 8 hours, 5 hours, 7 hours, and 6 hours. The apparent 5-hour anomaly did not make it into the headlines and is rarely mentioned to athletes. Of course there is much more to the story than that.

The researchers gathered two critical pieces of information, the number of reported injuries over 21 months and the average number of hours per night the students said they slept during the season. Collecting retrospective injury data from certified athletic trainers' records seems to be one of the best ways to collect such information. It did not depend on the recollections of athletes or their trainers, but was part of the written record at the time.

The collection of sleep data, however, is much different. The question seems simple enough, but it is not. The researchers acknowledged that one of the limitations of the study was that the sleep data came from simply asking the adolescents how many hours, on average, they slept. That is one of the worst ways to gather sleep data from teenagers (or anybody). Not just asking them to self-report their sleep, but to remember how long they had slept weeks or months ago.

Even adults, when they are asked the next morning, how long they slept the previous night, are often off by an hour. In 2012, Jennifer Girschik and her colleagues in Australia looked at the problem of self-reported sleep in 56 women 18 – 80 years old. They each wore a medical-grade actigraph for a week and then also self-reported their sleep. They concluded "that sleep questions typically used in epidemiologic studies do not closely correspond with objective measures of sleep as assessed using actigraphy." In other words, people are bad at knowing how long they sleep. They also found that all those who reported sleeping 6 hours or less actually slept more than 6 hours as measured by actigraphy. In contrast, those that reported sleeping 8 hours or more overestimated their sleep as compared to actigraphy.

Teenagers also pose some unique problems in self-reporting sleep. Teenagers tend to have erratic sleep hours, often sleeping less during the week and sleeping in on weekends. How are they to average those hours? They were not given any instructions on how to do that.

Milewski and his colleagues also acknowledged that their study only looked at self-reported chronic sleep and not acute sleep loss or even napping. In addition, sleep duration is often not the most important sleep variable when considering human performance. Sleep quality is often a more important factor and was not considered here at all.

A final issue with the Milewski study is that the researchers considered each sport to have an equal risk of injury. The school has 24 varsity sports teams including football, tennis, swimming, baseball, basketball, soccer, cheerleading and equestrian riding amongst others. There is no mention of which sports the athletes participated in or the time spent in each sport. What if the athletes who reported sleeping the longest played sports with low injury rates? Maybe the athletes with the lowest number of injuries simply played safer or non-contact sports!

Does poor sleep result in more injuries in adolescent or other athletes? Maybe, or maybe not. This research actually raises more questions than answers. It is, however, a good example of how little scrutiny there is of sleep research involving athletes, despite the widespread dissemination of the "results".

Prove It

Despite the danger of some researchers faking or fudging data, scientists have often considered that there is a way to prove their scientific discoveries are real. That is replication. It is quite simple. Other independent scientists repeat an experiment. If they get the same results, then perhaps you are onto something. Your results are on the road to validation.

That is certainly true for some observational science. Anyone can put a prism in a window and expose it to sunlight and get a rainbow of colours. And, they always appear in the same order: red-orange-yellow-green-blue-indigo-violet. Anyone can expose a plate covered with barium platinocyanide (if they happen to have it kicking around their lab) to high voltage electricity and the plate will always shimmer from x-rays. Anyone can place low voltage detectors on a (living) human head and detect brain waves. These experiments are all reproducible.

However, scientific experiments are often more complicated. They rely on specific techniques or equipment and normally involve complicated statistics. Still, replication is often considered the holy grail of scientific research. It is just not achieved very often.

Lloyd Hughes at the University of Dundee wrote in his 2014 paper, "The State of Science and Unreliable Research":

> In 2012, Amgen (an American drug company) attempted to replicate 53 pre-clinical oncology studies they considered land-mark papers in the basic science of cancer. Even when liaising closely with authors of the relevant papers, only 11% of the papers findings were replicated, a result described by the authors as "shocking". In 2011 Bayer (a German drug company) only managed to replicate a quarter of 67 seminal studies in an analysis of early in-house projects in the research fields of oncology, women's health and cardiovascular diseases.

Failing to replicate the results of scientific experiments does not necessarily mean that the original experiments are flawed or even fraudulent. While replication has been the goal, research scientists have begun to realize that it is not always achievable. Some even argue that it is not necessarily desirable.

Humans are a complicated biological system. Any experiment might miss accounting for one aspect that might not have even been known at the time. Humans make pretty bad lab rats. There are often too many variables to account for everything.

73.6% of all statistics are made up.

Mark Suster

Sports science is relatively new and research has some unique barriers. It is very difficult to get enough athletes to participate in a study, particularly if they have to take time out of their practice, training, or competition time. You need large numbers of subjects to find small differences that matter. Christine Aschwanden and Mai Nguyen writing for *FiveThirtyEight* in May 2018 summed it up nicely:

> Science is hard, and sports science is particularly so. If you want to study, say, whether a sports drink or training method can improve athletic performance, you have to recruit a bunch of volunteers and convince them to come into the lab for a battery of time–and energy–intensive tests. These studies require engaged and, in many cases, highly fit athletes who are willing to disrupt their lives and normal training schedules to take part. As a result, it's not unusual for a treatment to be tested on fewer than 10 people. Those small samples make it extremely difficult to distinguish the signal from the noise and even harder to detect the kind of small benefits that in sport could mean the difference between a gold medal and no medal at all.

Liam Mannix, writing for *The Sydney Morning Herald*, emphasizes this problem by giving examples of sports research that used small samples:

> The claim that foam rollers could help with sore muscles, made by a team in 2015 that included a Charles Sturt University researcher, was based on a study of just eight people.

> The AIS [Australian Institute of Sport] tested curcumin – a component of turmeric – on just 17 men playing

social football and basketball but were still able to report in 2015 the first empirical evidence that it too helped with muscle soreness.

And in 2019 a University of Technology Sydney researcher co-authored a paper that tested cold-water baths on just 11 Brazilian rugby players. They also helped with sore muscles, the team found.

With such a small number of subjects it would be difficult to find such significant results using classical statistical analysis that requires a 95% confidence of an association. But these researchers were using something different; a new form of statistical analysis, unique to sports science, called Magnitude-Based Inference (MBI), renamed in 2019 to Magnitude-Based Decisions (MBD).

This new system was designed by Will Hopkins, a highly respected physiologist with a PhD in neurophysiology. He spent a decade at the AIS as a visiting scholar, and according to Victoria University, has a part-time professional appointment there. Victoria University also summed up the basis of his work, "He is best known for rejecting statistical significance and replacing it with a clinically and practically more relevant method of inference based on uncertainty in the magnitude of effects."

The idea is that MBD will be able to find a significant relationship from small numbers of subjects where classical statistical analysis will not. It has been used in over 230 published sports science papers. However, MBD is not without its critics, particularly from classical statisticians.

Stephen Woodcock, a sports statistician at the University of Technology Sydney, calls MBD a "statistics cult". Andrew

Vickers, a statistician at Memorial Sloan Kettering Cancer Center, said, "'It's basically a math trick that bears no relationship to the real world. It gives the appearance of mathematical rigor', by inappropriately combining two forms of statistical analysis using a mathematical oversimplification."

In 2012, Emma Knight was working as a statistician at the AIS where Hopkins' new system was being used. She was getting a number of questions about how it worked that she couldn't answer. Knight convinced the AIS to bring in Alan Welsh, a highly regarded statistician from the Australian National University, to take a look.

Hopkins' MBI (MBD) system was embedded into an excel spreadsheet where researchers could simply input their data into the cells and get out answers as to any statistical association as well as other considerable statistical "bling" for publication. Welsh reverse engineered the spreadsheet and discovered that Hopkins' system had moved the goal posts of classical statistics from requiring a 95% confidence (5% due to chance) to a 50% confidence (50% it was due to chance). A coin flip. Heads there is an association, tails there is no association. No wonder he could find "associations" where classical statistics could find none. Welsh said, "They are claiming to have found effects that very likely are not real." As a result the AIS phased out the use of Hopkins' system.

Both Charles Sturt University and Victoria University continued to use and defend Hopkins' system. It is controversial. In the public back and forth between Hopkins and his detractors they appear to agree on one thing. That there seems to be a lack of education amongst researchers who use both classical statistical software and MBI (MBD) as to the underlying science and how to use the systems properly.

Of course, this begs the question – if researchers cannot agree on the appropriate statistics and what they mean, how do teams and athletes know what to believe? For athletes and teams there is so much sports research information it feels like drinking from a fire hose. There are no easy answers except for perhaps more education on evaluating scientific research and once an issue surfaces to re-evaluate what information is passed on to athletes and what information forms the basis of a sports science program. One of the concerns has been that shoddy science, once published, finds its way into team programs and into the psyche of coaches and remains there, despite revelations the research is bogus.

It is interesting to point out that Hopkins is highly respected in his field and that appears, as much as anything, to have driven the initial acceptance of his system without much scrutiny. The same could be said about Anversa's work with supposed heart stem cells and with Vollmer's work in promoting the lie detector. Scientific findings, particularly when driven by a personality, should be closely scrutinized especially when their findings seem to contradict scientific norms.

INCONVENIENT SLEEP

CHAPTER 6

The Skinny

There is considerable research into how sleep affects human performance. Poor sleep can result in poor performances and longer recovery times. This is not just theoretical or provable in a laboratory, but provable in the field.

Here we help athletes understand how the leading research can help them maximize their performance by setting realistic, individualized sleep goals.

For something so essential and basic, sleep has turned out to be a complicated biological nightmare for scientists.

Katherine Harmon

One of the most common questions asked by athletes is, "How much sleep do I need?" While that sounds like a simple question, it is not. Organizations like the American Academy of Sleep Medicine and the National Sleep Foundation and even government agencies provide guidelines or recommended sleep durations, based on age.

The recommendations are normally expressed as ranges. For newborns (0 -3 months) the range is 14 – 17 hours of sleep a day. For teenagers (14 – 17 years old) it is 8 – 10 hours, and for young adults (18 – 25 years old) and adults it is 7 – 9 hours. These ranges are based on broad public health concerns with the understanding that there are individual differences within those ranges. From a public health perspective you are getting "the right amount of sleep if [you], wake up feeling well rested and perform well during the day."

There are exceptions to the public health guidelines. For example, some people are able to function well with as little as 4 – 6 hours of sleep each night. In 2009, researchers in California discovered a genetic mutation in a mother and daughter that allowed them to function normally with only 6 hours of sleep. They were dubbed "short-sleepers". The rest of their family needed 8 hours of sleep.

In 2019, researchers mostly from the U.K. and the U.S. showed that there was a much bigger genetic component to sleep duration than previously thought. They analyzed genetic (DNA) data from 446,000 individuals and compared it to the subjects' self-reported sleep durations. Recognizing the limitations of self-reported sleep, they also looked at a subgroup of over 85,000 individuals who each wore an actigraph for a week to measure their sleep objectively. Their findings were quite astonishing.

They discovered 78 places on the DNA that affect how long people sleep. They concluded that an individual's sleep could vary about 22 minutes per night, based solely on genetic makeup.

Also in 2019, the original researchers who had discovered the short sleeper genetic mutation in 2009, reported a new study. This time the study showed there was a second "short sleep" gene which allowed the individuals with it to function normally throughout their lifetime. Genetically short sleeper are extremely rare. The lead researcher estimates that perhaps only one person in several thousand actually has a short sleep gene.

Likewise, there are natural "long-sleepers". Those that regularly sleep 10 – 12 hours a night and obtain good sleep quality without complaints. While it seems that there is little research on the human genetics of long sleepers Susan Harbison and her colleagues at the National Institutes of Health have performed a study on the genetics of fruit flies. That research, "established a clear genetic component to sleep duration, revealing mutants that convey very long or short sleep." "Until now, whether sleep at such extreme long or short duration could exist in natural populations was unknown." They "also found that the lifespan of the naturally long and short sleepers did not differ significantly from the flies with normal sleeping patterns. This suggests that there are few physiological consequences – whether ill effects or benefits – of being an extreme long or short sleeper."

For athletes that are not genetic short or long sleepers, which is the vast majority of athletes, there are health consequences to regularly sleeping too much or too little. Both are associated with obesity, type 2 diabetes, cardiovascular disease, depression and increased mortality from all causes.

Performance Consequences of Poor Sleep

In July 1997, two Australian researchers, Drew Dawson and Kathryn Reid, published some interesting research on sleep deprivation in *Nature*. They had 40 subjects stay awake for an extended period of time and had them take an objective reaction time test every 30 minutes. The subjects woke up at 8:00 am and stayed awake until noon the next day (28 total hours). Then after the subjects had recovered, the researchers took the same group and instead of keeping them awake for long hours, they gave them alcohol to drink. Starting at 8:00 am they began drinking 10-15 grams of alcohol (one to one and a half standard drinks) every 30 minutes until their blood alcohol level reached 0.10. While still taking a reaction time test every 30 minutes.

Dawson and Reid compared the reaction times of those that were awake for long hours to those that were drunk. On average, being awake for 17 straight hours produced the same reduced reaction time as having 0.05 BAC. Being awake for 24 hours produced the same reaction times as having 0.10 BAC. The researchers stated, "Our results underscore the fact that relatively moderate levels of fatigue impair performance to an extent equivalent to or greater than is currently acceptable for alcohol intoxication."

That study looked at keeping people awake for long hours to see how it affected their reaction time. In 2003, Hans Van Dongen and a team at the University of Pennsylvania School of Medicine undertook one of the most ambitious and comprehensive studies into how just reducing sleep hours affects performance.

Conducting research on human sleep is complex and requires researchers to understand and account for a myriad of medical, lifestyle, and environmental factors. It can be complicated, expensive, and time consuming to even attempt to understand simple questions concerning sleep and performance.

The Set-up

Instead of just keeping people awake for long hours Van Dongen and his team decided to restrict the amount of sleep people got and check their reaction times as the experiment progressed. They found 48 people between the ages of 21 - 38 who were willing to undergo strict experimental conditions for 3 weeks. This age group is typical of professional athletes.

Each of the 48 subjects had to undergo medical examinations prior to the study including clinical urine and blood tests and toxicology screening. None of the subjects had any medical issues, psychiatric or sleep related disorders and were also drug free. No one had worked regular night shifts or rotating shifts in the previous 2 years or had travelled across time zones in the previous 3 months.

In the 2 weeks prior to the experiment none of the subjects had consumed caffeine, alcohol, tobacco or medications. All of this was verified by blood and urine testing. In the 5 days prior to the start of the experiment all the subjects' slept at home and their sleep was monitored. They wore medical-grade actigraphs, kept sleep diaries of their activities and used time-stamped phone records showing when they got into and out of bed.

After spending 2 weeks just preparing for the experiment, the 48 subjects were ready to begin.

The Experiment

The subjects spent the next 20 nights at the sleep lab at the University of Pennsylvania, being monitored 24/7. For the first 3 nights all the subjects were given 8 hours in bed to sleep. This was to create a baseline and to ensure no one had a sleep debt. The subjects were then randomly broken up into 4 groups.

The first group underwent a more traditional sleep deprivation study. They were kept awake for 88 straight hours. That is 3 days and nights plus 16 hours. The other 3 groups were given 8 hours, 6 hours or 4 hours in bed each night for the next two weeks with everyone awake by 7:30 am. Their sleep and wake behaviours were constantly monitored.

Their sleep was measured by PSG as well as visual monitoring. During the times they were awake all the subjects were closely watched. They were only "allowed to read, watch movies, [or] interact with laboratory staff". They were not allowed vigorous activities (exercise). They were not allowed to nap. Every two hours, while awake, all the subjects had to take a 10-minute PVT (Psychomotor Vigilance Task), a simple reaction time test, as well as some tests for mental performance and subjective complaints.

Experiment #2

Meanwhile, at about the same time Van Dongen's work was underway Gregory Belenky and a team at the Walter Reed Army Institute of Research in Maryland were conducting a similar experiment. They found 66 volunteers between the ages of 24 – 62 to spend a total of 14 days in a laboratory having their sleep and reaction time and movement monitored throughout the day.

The volunteers were all in good health and had no neurological diseases or psychiatric or sleep disorders and no alcohol or drug addiction. No one was allowed to take any medications, including over the counter drugs for 48 hours before the start of the experiment. They were not allowed nicotine in any form and were allowed no more than 300-400 mg of caffeine per day (about 2 cups of coffee).

During the 14 days/nights in the laboratory none of the 66 volunteers were allowed to nap. The first three nights all of them were given 8 hours in bed to sleep. Then they were broken up into 4 groups for the next week. One group was allowed 3 hours in bed each night and the others 5 hours, 7 hours and 9 hours. After 7 days of sleep restriction all the groups were given 8 hours in bed (from 11 pm until 7am) for 3 nights to try to recover.

Throughout the entire experiment, except for the final night before going home, all their sleep was monitored using PSG and every few hours they took a PVT reaction time test.

Taken together these two experiments, to date, are the most comprehensive and controlled experiments demonstrating how reduced sleep can affect reaction times in healthy people. The results have a direct bearing on sports and provide some valuable lessons.

Lesson #1

For both experiments the results were largely the same. The less sleep the subjects obtained, the worse their reaction times.

Belenky also showed that 9 hours in bed (about 8 hours of sleep) for 7 straight nights was enough to consistently maintain reaction time at a high level. Similarly, Van Dongen showed that 8 hours in bed for 14 straight nights (about 7 hours of sleep), was enough to maintain reaction time at a high level without any degradation over time. While there are likely some individual differences, the studies taken together, show that 7 – 8 hours of actual sleep on a consistent basis is enough to maintain reaction time at a high level. Athletes may not need 9 or 10 hours of sleep to maximize their reaction time. They may, however, need 9 or 10 hours in bed to get the sleep they need.

Lesson #2

In the Belenky study, those that slept 5 – 6.5 hours a night showed an initial decline in reaction time for the first few days, then their reaction time stabilized, but at the lower level and stayed there. It didn't get worse and it didn't get better, even continuing to sleep 5 – 6.5 hours a night.

They also asked the subjects to self-report their sleepiness. What is fascinating about the results is that initially their subjective feelings from a lack of sleep reflected their actual sleep hours. They had lost sleep and felt it.

However, after a few days the subjects began to report feeling "normal" again. They still had low sleep hours but felt normal.

This is a phenomenon that can be called "re-norming". The subjects feels normal with reduced sleep hours, but have a slower reaction time. This is why it can be difficult to convince athletes who do not sleep well that they have a problem. They rely on their subjective feelings that they are okay, when they are not. Athletes do not often take an objective reaction time test (PVT) which can prove to them that their low sleep hours come at the cost of their reaction time.

The researchers concluded that the subjects' brains largely adapted to sleep loss by making them feel "normal". However, on objective PVT reaction tests they did not perform very well. Thus, creating an insidious situation where subjects get used to reduced sleep and think they are doing just fine.

Many athletes equate how they feel with how they can perform. It doesn't work that way!!

Recovery

One of the other major findings of the experiments involving the 3-, 5-, 7- and 9-hour in-bed group (Belenky), was how long it took to recover their reaction time following sleep loss. Only the 9 hours in bed (about 8 hours of sleep) group were able to maintain a consistent reaction time across all the days of the experiment. There was nothing to recover from. Their reaction time was consistent and good every day.

However, the subjects who slept less than 7 hours a night for a week could not regain their reaction time even with 3 nights of 8 hours in bed to recover.

addition, Van Dongen found that sleeping 6 hours or less per night for 14 nights produced reaction times comparable to 1 - 2 nights of total sleep deprivation. In other words, constantly sleeping low sleep hours can catch up to you. It is additive and difficult to recover from.

These experiments provide valuable insights into the difficulties many athletes have with travel and not sleeping well. Recovery is not easy and game scheduling, particularly with back-to-back and frequent games, can make it virtually impossible to fully recover reaction time during the season.

Napping

Napping is highly touted in the sports world and it is quite common for athletes to nap in the afternoon prior to an evening game or to nap to make up for sleep loss from travel. However, not all athletes nap or can nap, leading to some anxiety about not being able to keep up with their teammates. It is important for athletes to understand why they may not be able to nap in order to reduce any unnecessary anxiety.

Napping is often described as "short sleep" and is considered a "global phenomenon". One estimate states that 74% of U.S. young and middle-aged adults nap at least once a week. Despite this, the scientific research about how naps affect humans is seriously lacking.

In 2010, Australian researchers Nicole Lovato and Leon Lack analyzed what was known at the time about napping and its effects on performance. They concluded that people mostly nap because they had lost sleep and wanted to make up for it or because they anticipated losing sleep and wanted to prepare for it.

Their review also looked at how long people napped and what effect that had on their performance. They said that the benefits of a 5 – 15-minute nap was almost immediate and lasted 1 – 3 hours. However, naps longer than 30 minutes had a short-term problem: individuals would often wake up with "sleep inertia". The groggy, fuzzy-brained feeling when waking up from a deep sleep lasting 15 – 30 minutes. During that time performance is reduced. After the groggy feeling went away their performance increased and lasted for many hours.

They also looked at the best time to nap during the day. The conclusion was, "the preferred time to nap is usually reported to be during the post-lunch dip period between 1300 and 1600 h." Napping during other times was not as effective. They also said that people "who regularly nap seem to show greater benefits than those who rarely nap."

Finally, they noted some of the difficulties with nap research. There were only a few studies available and each one used different measures and methodologies, which makes it hard to compare data. It is also worth noting that some of the napping studies use 10 or less subjects. For example, one study on the effects of a 20-minute nap on performance had only seven young adults as subjects.

In 2018, Elizabeth A. McDevitt and her colleagues conducted a study involving 83 young, healthy people and suggested that there are individual differences in how napping affects performance. It was suggested that human genetics likely plays a role in napping similar to the genetic differences in how long people sleep. In other words, napping may not be a learned behaviour, but rather a genetic response.

In addition, they stated that about 50% of the U.S. population regularly nap and 50% do not nap. The researchers noted that those who nap regularly do not experience the groggy "sleep inertia" to the same degree that those who only nap occasionally do. In the minds of the researchers, "not all naps are equal."

Napping is sleep and can improve performance during nighttime games, particularly if the athlete is a regular napper and the nap takes place in the afternoon. However, if an athlete is not a regular napper it may be due to the individual's genetics and not from a lack of trying.

The napping research to date is far from definitive and leaves many questions unanswered. Further research is needed to answer basic questions for athletes, like how the duration of napping effects performance or if non-nappers do occasionally nap, whether that has any effect on their performance in the short-term or long-term. Sleep and performance research is difficult enough to conduct, napping research seems even harder.

Correlation Between Sleep and Learning

Nita Miller and Lawrence Shattuck wanted to see how much sleep recruits were getting at the United States Military Academy at West Point, New York and at the United States Navy's Recruit Training Command at Great Lakes, Illinois. They embarked on a 4-year study to find the answer. The recruits were all adolescents between the ages of 17 – 26. The ages of college student-athletes and many professional athletes.

At these military academies everything the recruits do is regimented: when they march, when they sleep, when they eat, when they train, when they study and when they play sports. At West Point there are about 1,300 new recruits every year that begin a four-year program. The researchers followed one class for their entire time at West Point beginning in 2004. All recruits completed questionnaires about their sleep and 80 were chosen to wear medical-grade actigraphs to measure sleep/wake cycles.

All recruits had their first mandatory formation at 6:45 am, although many had to wake up much earlier for athletic training. Miller and Shattuck found that sleep deprivation was pervasive at West Point. Specifically, they found that first year recruits slept an average of about 5 hours a night; second year recruits 5 ½ hours a night; third year recruits 5 ¾ hours a night and fourth year recruits about 6 hours a night. Overall, during the 4-year study 77% of the students slept between 4 and 7 hours per night. Only 11% slept more than 7 hours a night.

At the Navy's Great Lakes Academy Miller and Shattuck wanted to know how the recruits' sleep patterns affected academic performance. Up until 1980, the recruits were allowed 8 hours in bed every night to sleep. As the amount of materials and training exercises increased, the Navy decided to reduce the time available for sleep rather than extend the program beyond the normal 63 days. Recruits were, therefore, allowed only 6 hours of time in bed each night to sleep. Many did not even get that opportunity as they sometimes had to stand guard and be vigilant during the night.

Miller and Shattuck conducted a four-year study from 2000 – 2003 which tracked the changes in test scores as the available hours of sleep changed for the recruits. In 2001, the Navy

Admiral changed the sleep opportunity to 7 hours and in 2002 back to 8 hours a night. Even with 8 hours in bed to sleep Miller and Shattuck found, through the use of actigraphy, that the recruits really only slept about 6 – 6.5 hours a night. The researchers then went back through the massive number of standardized tests that the recruits had to take from 2000 – 2003. They compared average academic scores from 2000 and 2001 with six hours of sleep opportunity to 2003 when the recruits were given an 8-hour opportunity to sleep. The results were remarkable!

With an opportunity to sleep for 8 hours recruits scored, on average, 11% higher compared to the 6-hour groups. This has enormous implications for student-athletes in high school and college and for professional athletes. This study, amongst others, demonstrated that sleep affects the ability to learn and retain and use information. Think about trying to remember complex plays and strategies or to maintain grades to stay in school with little sleep!

The Division of Sleep Medicine at Harvard Medical School provided an explanation:

> First, a sleep-deprived person cannot focus attention optimally and therefore cannot learn efficiently. Second, sleep itself has a role in the consolidation of memory, which is essential for learning new information.

Sleep is seen as a necessary function to move information from short-term memory to long-term memory. The essence of learning. Poor sleep makes that difficult.

Athletic Performance

While the research indicates that sleep loss affects reaction time and academic performance the question remains: what is the evidence that sleep loss affects actual athletic performance during games? That was the challenging question Cheri Mah tried to answer many years ago. She would become a leading pioneer in the field.

Cheri Mah was a competitive dancer who grew up in Cupertino, California, more popularly known as part of the Silicon Valley and home to technology giants like Apple and Google. She had a passion for sports and followed in her family's footsteps by attending near-by Stanford University. Mah's brother had enrolled in William Dement's popular class "Sleep and Dreams" and passed on rave reviews that sparked her interest.

Her studies at Stanford led her to work in Dement's famous sleep research laboratory in the School of Medicine. He eventually became her mentor. This provided Mah with the opportunity to get involved with sleep and sport research. Van Dongen and Belenky's laboratory work addressed how sleep duration likely affected reaction time, but how did sleep actually affect athletic performance during games and practices? Mah wanted to find out.

The difficulty is you cannot construct the same sort of research project Van Dongen and Belenky had conducted in a laboratory in real world sports. They had asked people to sleep less and then test their reaction times. High-level athletes would never jeopardize their careers by restricting their sleep to see how poorly they might perform. Mah had a better idea. As a student she already knew that students, including student-athletes, were not sleeping as long as they should. What if the athletes were asked to sleep longer than they normally did? How would that affect their performance?

Being a pioneer in this area was not easy. Mah had to hang out in the weight room to befriend players, coaches, and trainers and to convince them to participate in her study. She eventually convinced the coaches, trainers and 11 players on the Stanford men's varsity basketball NCAA Division I team to participate. Mah designed the first study ever to examine increased sleep and athletic performance. It was not an easy study to conduct, but she had some help. William Dement, the father of modern sleep medicine, signed on. It was also a huge 7-week commitment for the basketball players during their playing season. It would be worth the effort. Some of those university players are now playing in the NBA and have acknowledged the benefits of being involved in Mah's study, which was published in 2011.

The players had to be healthy with no injuries; have no current difficulties with their sleep, no history of sleep or psychiatric disorders; not be taking medications with sleep side effects and not taking illicit drugs. During the 7 – 11 weeks of the study they had to sleep alone (except when travelling for away games) and not consume alcohol or caffeine. In addition, they had to wear a medical-grade actigraph 24/7 except during practices and games and keep a sleep diary, writing down when they went to sleep, when they woke up and any napping times. Finally, the players had to continue with their normal athletic and academic responsibilities.

The experiment itself was quite simple. For 2 weeks all the players would continue with their normal sleep routines. Following that, all the players would try to extend their normal sleep hours by spending at least 10 hours in bed each night. During the day the players would stay after practice to perform some routine exercises monitored by the coaches, trainers and Mah. After each practice the players would run a 282-foot timed sprint (baseline to half court, back to baseline then sprint to the end of the court and back), shoot 10 free throws, and 15 three-point shots (5 from each corner and 5 facing the basket). Mah collected data from their baseline (2 weeks) and sleep extension (5 – 7 weeks) periods and compared the results.

Mah found that the players were able to "extend" their sleep from their normal average of 6.5 hours during the baseline period to an average of 8.5 hours. As a result, the players (on average) were able to increase their sprint time by 0.7 seconds (about 4%), and their free throws and 3-point shots by 9% each.

One of the interesting (or disturbing) findings of the study was the self-reported sleep by the players. Because the players kept diaries and wore actigraphs Mah was able to determine that, on average, during the baseline phase, players over-estimated their sleep by 70 minutes per night and during the sleep extension 5 – 7-week period players over-estimated their sleep by 116 minutes (almost 2 hours) every night. This study demonstrates, yet again, that humans are not very good at estimating their own sleep. Mah relied on the sleep hours measured by actigraphs.

Mah's study demonstrates the difficulty in undertaking such research. It is impossible, outside the laboratory, to control for all the factors affecting sleep, in addition to actually measuring sleep without using PSG. There is little funding to carry out such studies. Nevertheless, Mah's study is still considered not only the first of its kind but the most comprehensive study demonstrating how sleep can affect athletic performance. Interestingly, the 8 or 8.5 hours of sleep obtained by the players during the sleep extension phase is close to the 8 hours of sleep (9 hours in bed) Belenky found that maximized and stabilized reaction times.

This experiment by Mah is one of the most quoted and referenced sleep and athletic performance studies to date. It is also one of the most "misquoted" studies on the subject. Virtually all of the references to this study from sports infographics to team presentations confuse "time in bed" with "actual sleep". The players did not obtain 10 hours of sleep during the sleep extension phase they spent 10 hours in bed and obtained 8 or 8.5 hours of actual sleep to increase their athletic performance in specific drills.

This confusion can create some anxiety amongst athletes who think they must obtain 10 or more hours of sleep every night in order to maximize their performance. The current research shows that, on average, 8 or 9 hours of sleep is sufficient.

It is common for athletes and coaches to complain that extending or enhancing sleep is a burden to the athlete and impractical in real life situations. Mah disagreed:

> Another important feature of this study is that it was conducted during the NCAA season and included an athlete's occasional variable daily schedule of practices, games, and travel. By monitoring collegiate athletes during an actual competitive season, this study accurately reflects the potential improvements that sleep extension can have on athletic performance despite the inconsistent schedule of collegiate and professional sports. Furthermore, athletes were able to fulfill their typical personal, work, and training activities and

obligations while also extending their total sleep time. In so doing, this study shows that extended sleep is realistically obtainable during training and competition.

While Mah says that getting sufficient sleep is "realistically obtainable" for college athletes her 2018 study of 628 student-athletes from 29 varsity sports at Stanford University showed that they are not getting the sleep they need. About 40% were getting less than 7 hours of sleep during the week and 51% reported excessive daytime sleepiness. Interestingly, these numbers are not too different from the ones found by Nita Miller some 10 years earlier at West Point. It appears not much has changed in the last decade with regards to the sleep habits of college-age students.

Don't Hold Your Breath

The human brain craves sleep like it craves oxygen. Both are vital to the proper functioning of the brain. However, our brain gives us leeway. Humans often restrict the amount of sleep they get because their brain allows it. Perhaps it is a defence mechanism. If we were to fall asleep when it becomes dark and only be able to wake up when it was light out, we might become some predator's meal. We can stay awake for long hours and wake up from sleep to defend ourselves.

There is a children's game where friends sit around and see who can hold their breath the longest. At some point each person begins to breathe. The human brain allows us to restrict the amount of oxygen available to the brain but when it becomes critically low the brain takes over and forces us to breath. Sleep is very much the same. The brain will tolerate only so much sleep loss before it takes over and forces you to fall asleep.

When we stay awake for long periods of time or restrict our sleep, we pay a health and safety price and a performance price. While our brain lets us get away with reducing our sleep there is a cost to it. Holding your breath is not much different. While controlled breathing is an important tool in sports can you imagine trying to play a sport while holding your breath?

There is still individual variability in sleep need (leaving aside the few people who might be genetic long or short sleepers). That is, an individual might be able to maximize their reaction time with 7 hours of good sleep while another might need 9 hours. The problem for athletes is that most do not know how much sleep they need to maximize their reaction time. They simply try to maximize their sleep hours. The difficulty with that approach is that they don't know what their maximum is. Some athletes may very well be able to reach peak performance with 7 hours of sleep but feel pushed to get more creating unnecessary anxiety.

There are ways to determine individual sleep needs by taking a cue from the Van Dongen and Belenky experiments. Athletes could measure their simple reaction time over several days or weeks to demonstrate how their sleep hours affect their performance. This would give them individual objective data to better understand their own sleep need. That, however, takes time and commitment.

Finally, there is another aspect to maximizing human performance that is often misunderstood. That is circadian rhythms which play a part in determining daily changes in reaction time and when athletes sleep.

INCONVENIENT SLEEP

CHAPTER 7

The Time of Day

The human body is complex, a lot more complex than many athletes realize. Every cell in our bodies has a clock and each of these clocks is regulated and orchestrated by a master clock in our brains. We explore how these clocks interact with each other and how they control everything from body temperature, to the effectiveness of medications, to athletic performance.

"The body is essentially a collection of clocks."

Satchidananda Panda, Professor, Salk Institute for Biological Studies

In the 1950s people throughout the world feared two things: the nuclear bomb and polio. Nuclear bombs had been dropped by the U.S. (to end World War II) onto two Japanese cities in 1945 killing hundreds of thousands of people. By the late 1940s the Soviet Union had its own nuclear weapon and the Soviet Union and the United States were in a "Cold War". People across the globe feared a nuclear war that could kill millions of people.

Polio was equally feared because it was invisible and more insidious. Polio is an infectious disease causing, amongst other things, irreversible paralysis, particularly in young children. Polio has sometimes been referred to as "The Crippler". It is caused by a virus and is contagious. In 1952 alone, there were about 60,000 U.S. children infected. There was no cure. By 1955 Jonas Salk had developed an effective vaccine and infection rates dropped. By 1979 the polio virus was eliminated in the U.S.

However, infection rates globally began to increase again and by the 1980s there was an estimated 350,000 cases from 125 countries. Finally, in 1988, the Global Polio Eradication Initiative was founded and began its campaign of education and vaccination. By 2013, the number of polio cases had been reduced by 99.99% to just 407 cases.

People today still fear nuclear bombs but polio has largely been eradicated and often forgotten, although there are still occasional outbreaks in developing countries.

Today, Jonas Salk is not exactly a household name. But, in the 1950s and 60s he was a scientific rock star. He had found a way to prevent a very scary disease. Salk was born in New York City in 1914. His parents had immigrated from Eastern Europe and had little education. Salk was talented and hard-working and was able to attend the City College of New York, as the tuition was free. He went on to graduate from medical school at New York University. He decided to research viruses and eventually put together a team that developed the vaccine for polio in 1955.

A few months after the discovery *The New York Times* wrote, "Salk is profoundly disturbed by the torrent of fame that has descended upon him. ... He talks continually about getting out of the limelight and back to his laboratory... because of his genuine distaste for publicity, which he believes is inappropriate for a scientist."

In 1954, the Nobel Prize "was awarded to John Enders, Thomas Weller, and Frederick Robbins for their discovery of the ability of poliovirus to grow in cultures of various types of tissue. This discovery was a milestone in virology because it not only lead *(sic)* to the production of both killed and live poliovirus vaccines, but it allowed the growth of many other viruses." It was a necessary stepping stone to the discovery of the polio vaccine.

Salk was nominated for the Nobel Prize in 1955 and 1956. He was turned down both times. In 1955, Salk's polio vaccine was still in clinical trials and they wanted to wait for the results before proceeding. In 1956, the Nobel committee relied on an opinion from Sven Gard, a professor of virology at the Karolinska Institute, who said, "Salk has not in the development of his methods introduced anything that is principally new, but only exploited discoveries made by others." He concluded, "Salk's publications on the poliomyelitis vaccine cannot be considered as Prize worthy". It seems a bit like awarding the prize to those that invented coloured paint but not to the person that uses it to paint a masterpiece. Nevertheless, Salk was a dedicated researcher and he retreated to his lab to continue his work.

In the late 1960s Salk and other polio researchers, including Gard, were again nominated for a Nobel Prize for their work on polio vaccines. "Gard refused to be nominated, saying that the work was not primary but depended on accomplishments of those who had already received the Prize; this effectively killed the nomination." Salk was never nominated again.

Salk was a passionate researcher and had a dream to "create a collaborative environment where researchers could explore the basic principles of life and contemplate the wider implications of their discoveries for the future of humanity." Research to discover the natural world for the betterment of mankind, not for profits. He made his dream come true by creating the Salk Institute for Biological Studies in California.

In 1960, the City of San Diego gifted Salk 27 acres of oceanfront property. The institute continues to be supported by the National Institutes of Health, the March of Dimes, and numerous private foundations and individuals. Salk brought on many distinguished scientists including Francis Crick, the co-discoverer of the structure of DNA. They were intent on conducting pure research that could benefit everyone.

Today the Salk Institute is divided into 16 different research laboratories. In the Regulatory Biology Laboratory, Professor Satchidananda Panda, focuses on circadian rhythms and is making ground-breaking discoveries that apply to all sports.

The Human Clock

At the time the City of San Diego gifted the land to the Salk Institute the field of chronobiology (how time affects biology) was coming of age.

Across the country on the north shore of Long Island, New York, the Cold Spring Harbor Laboratory held a symposium of leading chronobiology researchers that effectively kicked off and organized the field. One of the leading scientists was Franz Halberg, a researcher at the University of Minnesota. Halberg had coined the term "circadian" meaning changes during a day, a 24-hour cycle. His pioneering work in the field earned him the title, "Father of American Chronobiology".

The human brain contains billions of brain cells. The exact number is a little uncertain; depending on how they are counted, however, estimates range from 86 – 100 billion cells. They largely communicate with each other by electrical and chemical signals. The electrical signals were the ones found by Berger and form the basis of the sleep analysis using PSG.

In the depths of the human brain a group of about 20,000 brain cells coordinate just about everything we do; it is called the biological clock. (If you care, that group of cells is called the suprachiasmatic nucleus). Those cells coordinate the timing of "sleep-wake cycles, hormone release, eating habits and digestion, body temperature" and many other bodily functions, largely related to sleep. They take their cue from light. The cells are directly connected to our eyes and exposed to light and dark cycles. When it is dark out it tells the biological clock to get the body ready for bed and sleep. When it is light out it tells the biological clock to get the body up and going.

In 2017, Jeffrey Hall, Michael Rosbash and Michael Young were awarded the Nobel Prize for Physiology or Medicine for their work in chronobiology. They had figured out exactly how the master biological clock in our brain works; the clock genes make "proteins, whose levels rise and fall in a regular cyclic pattern. The proteins accumulate during the night and are used up during the day.

In 2019, Panda and colleagues at the Salk Institute discovered that when bright light hits our eyes it sends messages to our brains down two different pathways. One pathway tells the brain to rapidly close the pupil of the eye. This takes about a second. The other pathway is much slower and goes to the biological clock. Panda explained that the signal to the brain to constrict the pupil is "similar to water pouring out of a garden hose", extremely fast. However, the signals to the biological clock are "weaker – more like drip irrigation":

> This research helps explain why, when you get up in the
> night to get a drink of water and turn on the light for
> a few seconds, you're usually able to go right back to
> sleep," Panda says. "But if you hear a noise outside and
> end up walking around your house for half an hour with
> the lights on, it's much harder. There will be enough light
> signal reaching the master clock neurons in the brain
> that ultimately wakes up the rest of the brain.

In 2018, Panda and his colleagues published a study in the journal *Science* where they found that 80% of human genes follow a day/night rhythm. Panda was right when he said we are a collection of clocks. The time of day matters for many things.

Panda's work on hair growth helps explain the complexities of our many biological clocks:

Every time hair cells divide, they pick up DNA damage that needs to be repaired. The scientists discovered that mice hair cells repair that damage primarily in the evening. This process is akin to using a kitchen dishwasher, Panda says. 'Most of us run the dishwasher after we have accumulated a lot of dirty dishes – we don't run it every time a dish is dirty. The same is true for cells. They clean up – repair their DNA – at one time each day,' Panda says.

Radiotherapy [radiation therapy for cancer treatment] damages DNA in cells that divide rapidly, which is why it is used against growing cancer cells. That means that DNA damage to hair cells from radiotherapy delivered in the morning is not repaired until the evening, leading to hair loss. Damage from radiotherapy at night, however, is minimized because hair cells, already in the process of repairing DNA, can quickly heal.

'While we don't yet know if human hair follows that same clock we found in mice hair, it is true that facial hair in men grows during the day, resulting in the proverbial 5 o'clock shadow. There is no 5 a.m. shadow if you shave at night,' Panda says.

Jet Lag

These unique 20,000 brain cells, the "biological clock", act as the master clock for all our biological functions. A team at the Salk Institute, headed by Panda, figured out how the cells communicate and why they can be slow to respond to changes in light exposure, causing jet lag.

The tightly bunched brain cells buffer against rapid changes from the environment. They are not in a hurry to change the body's entire biological system onto a new schedule. These coordinated brain cells are slow to react to many things including changes in light.

The team at Salk found one gene that is particularly sensitive to light and is responsible for generating and maintaining circadian rhythms in the master biological clock. It is often called the "jet lag gene". This gene generates proteins that make all the other brain cells in the biological clock work together to produce coordinated circadian rhythms. It is like a symphony leader making all the cells perform together. These coordinated circadian rhythms send signals throughout the body that ensure various bodily functions maintain a 24-hour rhythm.

If the gene is removed so it cannot coordinate all the brain cells, then each cell follows its own individual clock. They act on their own and can rapidly change the body's biological system in response to light exposure.

When the jet lag gene was removed from mice, they all died in the womb. When the gene was removed during later development, they struggled to maintain normal circadian rhythms. Without the "jet lag gene" there is no coordination of the master clock brain cells and therefore the brain cells can react rapidly to light and dark cycles. That makes it easier to overcome jet lag but throws the body's circadian rhythms that control all of the timing of our biological functions into chaos.

This discovery helps explain why it has been so difficult to find ways to prevent jet lag. Rapid travel across multiple time zones introduces new light and dark cycles to the master clock causing jet lag. However, the tightly bunched brain cells are simply in no hurry to make changes. This makes sense because prior to modern modes of travel, it is doubtful that there was any evolutionary need to make rapid changes to the timing of our biological systems from the 24-hour dark – light cycles we normally experience.

Injury Clock

The human body has numerous clocks that also regulate repair mechanisms which seem to follow a circadian rhythm. For example, medical researchers from the U.K. looked at burns from 118 people and discovered that they healed faster in the daytime than at night:

> Burns that happened at night took an average of 60% longer to heal than burns that occurred during the day, with night-time burns (8pm to 8am) classed as 95% healed after an average of 28 days, compared to only 17 days if the burn happened in the day (8am to 8pm).

The researchers stated, "Our experimental results correlate with the observation that the time of injury significantly affects healing after burns in humans, with daytime wounds healing ~60% faster than night-time wounds."

The reason for this phenomenon is that skin cells simply move to the damaged site faster to repair it during the day than at night. In some ways that is not surprising. Humans are biologically programmed to be awake in the daytime and to sleep at night. Why waste time on having repair mechanisms for injuries that occur at night when you are supposed to be asleep?

Medication Clock

In October 2019, researchers at the University of Vigo in Spain published an interesting study. They followed over 19,000 patients for 4 to 8 years who were taking medications for high blood pressure. They divided the patients into two groups. One took their medication at bedtime and the other took their medication in the morning. During the study 1,752 patients experienced a cardiovascular event like a heart attack or stroke.

The researchers found:

> After taking into account factors such as age, sex, smoking status, history of cardiovascular events and typical decrease in blood pressure when asleep, the team found patients who took their medication at bedtime had a 56% lower risk of death from cardiovascular disease, a 49% lower risk of stroke and a 44% lower risk of heart attack compared with the other group.

They also said that those who took their medication before bed "showed better kidney function and cholesterol measures." It was felt that this timing was due to the patients' circadian rhythms. They were simply able to make better use of the drugs at night than in the morning. The lead researcher, Ramón Hermida, said, "'The same antihypertensive medication, the same molecule, at the same dose, ingested at two different times have totally different pharmacokinetics and pharmacodynamics and therefore they behave as two totally different medications.'"

Panda and his team also found that about 80% of FDA-approved drugs operate on a circadian rhythm. That is, they are more effective during certain times of the day or night than others.

The Temperature Clock

In 1950, some three years before the discovery of REM sleep, Nathaniel Kleitman discovered that body temperature can affect human performance:

> Contrary to popular opinion, one is not at his best, or most wide-awake, in the morning. Immediately upon getting up, one's performance is, as a rule, about as poor as it was the night before, prior to going to bed. During the course of the day there is a gradual increase in alertness, with a peak or plateau in the middle of the waking period, followed by a gradual decline in performance to a bed-time low.

Kleitman went on to say that human performance paralleled the rises and falls in body temperature. While this phenomenon has been studied by various researchers since then, a 2002 article by Kenneth Wright Jr. at the University of Colorado and his colleagues explained that when body temperature is higher, people show increases in "working memory, subjective alertness, visual attention", and sometimes reaction times.

It is particularly important for athletes to understand that their reaction time can vary as much as 10% a day based on the time of day and that these changes are similar to the changes in body temperature which can vary about 1 degree Celsius in a 24-hour period.

One interesting aspect of these changes is what is often called the "post-lunch dip." It's a period in the early afternoon when people often feel tired or sleepy. This is a natural part of human circadian rhythms and during those times body temperature drops, reaction times worsen, and people often feel like a nap. This is why, in some cultures, napping in the afternoon is a routine part of their day (siesta). This is also the time when many professional athletes, who play games in the evening, have naps.

The Athletic Performance Clock

Our bodies expect us to be awake in the daytime and to sleep at night. All our circadian rhythms follow that pattern. We also know that a lack of good sleep can affect reaction time and athletic performance. An interesting question is, does the timing of when you sleep and when you wake up matter?

In 2015, Elise Facer-Childs and Roland Brandstaetter from the School of Biosciences at the University of Birmingham in the U.K. argued that better athletic performance is determined, not by sleep, but by when the athlete normally wakes up.

The researchers were aware that the difference between winning or losing in sports is small:

> In the sports world, a competitive advantage can be as little as 1%; at the 2008 Beijing Olympics, for example, a 1% increase in the 9.93 s time gained by fourth place in the men's 100 m sprint would have resulted in the silver medal. Similarly, for the women's road race, 400 m swim, and 400 m sprint, a 1% improvement would have won a gold medal for the fourth-place competitor.

Through a screening process they found 20 competitive field hockey players who had similar fitness levels and ages (20 years old). The researchers knew that in the general population people fell into three broad categories. Those that normally wake up early and go to bed early, called "larks", those that normally stay up late and sleep in, called "owls" and those in-between. Generally, it is considered that about 25% of the population are "larks", 25% are "owls" and 50% are in between, in the overall population.

Through questionnaires, including sleep diaries, the researchers were able to sort the 20 athletes into to the three categories. Five were "owls", five were "larks" and ten were in-between. During the week the "owls" typically went to sleep at midnight and woke up at 9:30 am, the "larks" went to sleep at 11 pm and woke up at 7 am and the in-between group went to sleep at 11:30 pm and woke up at 8 am.

Six times a day each athlete took a "BLEEP" test to determine physical fitness:

> The BLEEP test is a progressive aerobic cardiovascular endurance test widely used by sports coaches to estimate athletes' maximum oxygen uptake, i.e., cardiovascular fitness, one of the most important components of physical fitness.

They reported the results for the 20 athletes. Overall, the athletes had their lowest performance at 7 am and intermediate performances at 10 am, 1 pm, and 10 pm. The athletes performed their best at 4 pm and 7 pm. Based solely on the time of day, there was an 11% difference between the lowest and highest average performances.

However, when they looked at the results of the BLEEP test by "type" (owl, lark or in-between) and by the number of hours after their respective normal wake up times the results were startling. The "larks" had their highest average performance about 5.6 hours after waking up, the in-between group about 6.5 hours after waking up, and the "owls" at approximately 11 hours after awakening.

What is most startling, was the difference in BLEEP test performances for each group individually throughout the day. During the day, both the "larks" and the in-between group had a difference of 7 – 10% between their best score and their worst score. However, for the "owls" the average performance difference throughout the day was 26%!!

The researchers proclaimed that personal best athletic performance could be achieved by paying attention to whether an athlete is an "owl", "lark" or "in-between" and how many have hours passed since their normal wake up time. While the number of participants in the experiment were quite low the results are something to consider.

Do Statistics Rule?

Roger Smith and a team from the Stanford University Sleep Disorders Clinic took a different, more statistical approach. Instead of looking at individual athlete measurements they focused on team win/loss records at different times of the day. Their theory was that teams playing games when their reaction time is fastest (late afternoon/early evening) should win more games than when teams play when their reaction time is slowest (morning/late evening).

They chose to look at Monday Night Football games in the National Football League over 25 years. Monday Night Football games are unique in that they are always played at 9 pm Eastern Standard Time (6 pm Pacific Time), regardless of where in the country they are actually played. Games are played all over the country and between teams from the same and different time zones, depending on the season. Smith and his team only focused on games played between East Coast and West Coast teams. Over the 25-year period (1970 – 1994) they found and analysed 63 games.

Whether a team wins or loses any single game is dependent on a wide range of variables, including talent, coaching, injuries, motivation, refereeing, and much more. Just like the many factors that affect individual performance which are very difficult to control in a field experiment, so are the factors affecting team win/loss records. Smith explained how they were able to reduce the impact of those variables:

> To reduce the confounding variables in this study, a comparison was made with the Las Vegas point spread for each game. The point spread essentially makes both teams equal by adding a certain number of points to the weaker team's score to ensure that an equal amount of money will be wagered on each team. Prior to each game, the point spread is carefully calculated by weighing the variables affecting each team's predicted performance (team record, injury reports, home-field advantage, winning streaks, playing surface, etc.).

The results were fascinating. West Coast teams won 63.5% of their Monday Night Football games whereas the East Coast teams only won 36.5% of those games.

The researchers also looked at the same teams' overall league win/loss records during those 25 years. The West Coast teams won 59.3% of their home games and the East Coast teams, 56.5% of their home games. There seems to be a small "home field" advantage, except for the East Coast Monday Night Football games.

Even more compelling, they found that when the East Coast teams played a non-West Coast team on Monday Night Football, their winning percentage at home increased by 23.7% to 67.5%. Similarly, when the West Coast teams played teams other than East Coast teams their home winning percentage dropped by 12.9% to 58.1%.

For gamblers, the researchers noted that, "In this 25-year sample, simply selecting a WC [West Coast] team without considering any other variable successfully predicted the winner against the point spread 67.9% of the time." A huge gambling win percentage by any standard.

Football Part 2

In 2013, Smith, then at Harvard Medical School, added Cheri Mah to his research team to conduct a follow-up study. They examined all East vs. West Coast matchups in the NFL that occurred at 8 pm Eastern Time (or later), not just Monday Night Football games. Combining the data from their original work they ended up reviewing 106 games from over 40 years of NFL games and 293 daytime games (start times at 1 pm and 4 pm EST).

Using the same point spread analysis, they discovered a significant difference between nighttime and daytime games. The West Coast teams "beat the point spread in 70 games vs.

36 games for EC [East Coast] teams" when playing at night. However, there was no significant difference between the East Coast vs. West Coast teams during the day games. Out of the 293 daytime games the West beat the point spread in 143 games and the East in 150 games.

Smith and his team said that, "Our use of the point spread to reduce the effects of potential confounding variables suggests that circadian factors are grossly under-recognized and underappreciated." While it is very difficult to predict the outcome in any single game, a long-term statistical analysis of NFL games shows that paying attention to circadian factors (time of day) can pay long-term benefits to teams.

Baseball Part 1

Chris Winter, at the Martha Jefferson Hospital Sleep Medicine Center, has had an interest in sleep/fatigue and circadian rhythms in the MLB for some time. Winter and his team conducted a review of 24,121 MLB games from 1997 – 2006, sponsored by Major League Baseball. The league and researches were interested in finding out if teams had a "circadian advantage" based on their travel and win/loss records. In other words, would the data show that a team would win more games in which they played when their circadian rhythm is closer to their current time zone compared to the circadian rhythm of their opponents?

Major League Baseball teams play 162 games per season, 81 at home and 81 away. They criss-cross the United States (and Toronto, Canada) from the East Coast to the West Coast and in-between. Sometimes they play teams in their home time zone and sometimes they play against teams up to a three hours' time difference away.

Winter's analysis showed that only 21% of all MLB games were played where one team had "a circadian advantage" (being closer to time zone acclimation than their opponent). With a one hour "advantage" or circadian rhythm closer to the current location the team with the advantage won 51.7% of the games. Teams with a 2-hour advantage won 51.8% of the games and teams with a 3-hour advantage won 60.6% of their games. The researchers also noted that the direction of travel mattered. Teams travelling West to East won 53% of their games and teams travelling East to West won 50.9% of their games.

Winter acknowledged that the research might have been more powerful if they had used the Las Vegas point spread as Smith had done in the NFL. Nevertheless, his research reveals the direction of travel can affect the outcome as can the number of time zones crossed before playing a game.

Baseball Part 2

In 2017, Alex Song and colleagues from Northwestern University published a similar study, "How jet lag impairs Major League Baseball performance". They analysed 46,535 MLB games over 20 years (1992 – 2011). They "observed that jet-lag effects were largely evident after eastward travel with very limited effects after westward travel."

They also found that an East Coast team travelling home from the West Coast would experience jet lag and lose their home field advantage if they played right away. They also said that the vast majority of the effects of jet lag for both away and home teams, "could be explained by a single measure, home runs allowed." They offered a solution:

> The results on the effect of jet lag on home runs allowed suggest that teams may want to change their travel protocol to mitigate this effect. For instance, a starting pitcher scheduled for a game in which the team is jet lagged might travel to the game location a few days ahead of the team, to adjust to the new time zone.

The Athlete

Laboratory studies have shown that sleep quality, duration, and timing can affect reaction time during the day. In addition, reaction time varies during the day due to circadian factors and jet lag. While there are many "solutions" to athletes' sleep problems, depending on the diagnosis, there are actually no validated "solutions" to jet lag for individual athletes.

An April 2020 review by 14 researchers published in the British Journal of Sports Medicine on, "How to manage travel fatigue and jet lag in athletes? A systematic review of interventions" concluded:

> We found no literature pertaining to the management of travel fatigue. Evidence for the successful management of jet lag in athletes was of low quality. More field-based studies specifically on athlete populations are required with a multifaceted approach, better design and implementation to draw valid conclusions.

In other words, the science has not evolved enough in the area of jet lag and circadian rhythms to provide validated solutions to athletes. There certainly are a number of publications purporting to help athletes "deal with jet lag" but their solutions all seem to be theory-based and not based on the results of well-designed and executed research into jet lag solutions.

CHAPTER 8

....

Moving Forward

Strength and conditioning programs have evolved over the decades and are now an integral part of every sports team globally. Sleep science is new. The integration of sleep into the activities of sports teams requires new thinking and the willingness to adapt to new technology and new concepts. Here we explore how initiators of sleep programs can learn from strength and conditioning programs and discuss the challenges ahead.

"I have never taken any exercise, except sleeping and resting, and I never intend to take any. Exercise is loathsome. And it cannot be any benefit when you are tired; I was always tired."

Mark Twain

One of the most important factors to team success is the physical conditioning of athletes. Every college and professional sports team has a strength and conditioning expert to design and implement the right program for individual players during the season and sometimes during the off-season. Teams spend millions of dollars on the best equipment and facilities and try to recruit the best staff. According to *USA Today* some of the 131 NCAA Division I football programs pay their strength and conditioning coaches handsomely. Its published list of salaries from 2019 shows the top 10 salaries averaged $591,820 per year. The top paid strength and conditioning coach, Chris Doyle from the University of Iowa, tops out at $800,200. Having athletes in top physical condition is a major priority for all sports teams, some are just more willing to pay more for the top talent to make that happen.

However, fifty years ago, strength and conditioning programs were unheard of. Since then they have undergone a significant evolution. Their modern history can be traced back to circuses in the late 19th century and the first few decades of the 20th century. The circuses would show off strongmen performing acts of strength like bending iron bars. Weightlifting gained widespread acceptance in Russia and Eastern Europe which dominated weightlifting sports for many decades. In the West, the emphasis was largely on aerobics particularly during the 1980s. Kenneth Cooper, a U.S. Air Force flight surgeon, published his book, "Aerobics" in 1968 that set off the craze. He believed that "strength training promoted a beautiful body but did nothing for health." Eventually the two schools of thought merged into modern strength and conditioning programs.

Prior to the 1970s strength and conditioning programs did not really exist in professional and college sports. Athletes were largely left on their own as teams exerted no control over individual athletes' strength and conditioning. All of that changed when Boyd Epley emerged onto the scene. Born in 1947 in Pawnee City, Nebraska with a population of about 1,600, Epley would go on to be the center of the universe for strength and conditioning globally. He literally helped invent the industry.

As a child, Epley was asthmatic and (in those days) asthmatics were often advised to move to drier, warmer climates. His family moved from Nebraska to Phoenix, Arizona where his father taught him weightlifting and body building at an early age. In high school he excelled at football but ended up receiving a scholarship in track and field as a pole vaulter in his home state at the University of Nebraska. There "he set a school record of 21 feet". In his senior year he suffered a back injury and retreated to the weight room to recover. He was no longer going to have a track and field career, or a football career for that matter.

Epley found himself interacting with football players and began teaching them the weightlifting techniques he learned from his father. The "weight room" was 416 sq. ft. and consisted of a few barbells. Pretty rudimentary, but if you just want to build muscle you don't need much.

At that time Bob Devaney was the head football coach at the University of Nebraska. The football team had been struggling. In 1968, they lost to their rival Oklahoma 47–0 on national television. It was a historic and embarrassing loss. The coach was looking for any help he could get. At that time there was a widely held belief in sports that strength training and speed were mutually exclusive. If you gained strength, you slowed down. On the advice of one of his assistant coaches he asked Epley to work with all the players to improve their strength. It was worth the gamble. He needed to make changes and was willing to experiment. In August 1969, he hired Epley as the first full-time strength and conditioning coach in any sport. At Epley's hiring, coach Devaney famously shook his hand and said, "If anyone gets slower you're fired." Epley was paid two dollars an hour. Thus began the decades-long global evolution of strength and conditioning programs in sport.

Epley set to work at the University of Nebraska and over the next 30 plus years he created and transformed strength and conditioning programs globally. In his first season the team record improved to 9–2 and they redeemed themselves by defeating Oklahoma 44–14. In 1970 and 1971 they won back-to-back national championships. Other teams began paying attention.

At that time there were no strength and conditioning programs, no certifications, no university degrees on the subject, and little if any research. All that was available in college sports was the program Epley was developing at Nebraska based on his own experiences. Soon other teams began hiring Epley's assistants to employ his systems. By 1978, some 9 years after Epley was first hired at Nebraska, there were 75 other people working in the field around the United States. Epley compiled their names in the National Directory of Strength Coaches and invited them to Lincoln, Nebraska to "unify, professionalize and promote greater performance and fitness of varsity athletes". Three years later, in 1981, the group changed its name to the National Strength and Conditioning Association. Today its membership includes over 45,000 members globally.

Major League Baseball was not much different than football in accepting and developing strength and conditioning programs. By the late 1970s only three teams had started programs. The Cincinnati Reds, the Philadelphia Phillies and the Houston Astros.

The Reds were quite successful at the time and known as the "Big Red Machine". Their program was developed and run by their athletic trainer, Larry Starr. Starr had a bachelor's degree in physical education and a master's degree in secondary education from Ohio University. He emphasized sports nutrition and strength and conditioning, something unheard of at the time in Major League Baseball.

The Philadelphia Phillies engaged a trainer with a different background. Gus Hoefling was an expert in martial arts. He trained the son of the owner of the Phillies in martial arts and also worked with future hall of fame pitcher Steve Carlton from the Phillies. Those connections eventually evolved into Hoefling using his martial arts background to provide physical training to the entire team.

In the late 1970s the Houston Astros minor league field coordinator was a marathon runner. He normally ran 15 miles a day. At training camp in Florida, he challenged the young players to run 5 miles a day. After a few days, the players were too sore to practice. They were out of shape. "The organization had spent a lot of money to bring these kids into Florida but couldn't do anything with them."

The Astros tried to resolve the situation by reaching out to Gene Coleman who was teaching weight training at Texas Tech University and The University of Texas at Austin. In addition, Coleman was a visiting scientist at NASA and "was involved in the astronaut testing program". In 1978, he was hired by the Astros as their head strength and conditioning coach. He had to start from scratch. The team had lots of room for the players to stretch, but no strength or conditioning equipment at all: no weights, no medicine balls, no stability balls. Nothing. He also realized that there was no baseline physical data or standards for ball players. Not just at the Astros, but in all of Major League Baseball. Coleman had a lot of work to do. He set out with the support of the team manager Bill Virdon, an ex-marine and an advocate of strength and conditioning. Virdon told the team:

> You might make excuses that you got thrown out because you[r] legs were sore from lifting or that you hung a slider because you were tired from running. But those might be the only positive things that you did for yourself off the field. Before you knock on my door to complain, you better be able to tell me that you got eight hours of sleep, ate three meals a day and avoided alcohol for at least a week before your bad performance. If you can lead a clean life and still think th[at] staying in shape inhibits your performance, I'll listen to you.

Vern Gambetta had more than a front row seat to observe the evolution of strength and conditioning programs, he lived it. He earned his Bachelor of Arts degree from California State University, Fresno in 1968 where he majored in Latin American history and minored in physical education. He started as a high school track coach but soon moved on to earn a master's degree from Stanford University in physical education. He then began a long coaching career that has lasted over 50 years. He has also authored 8 books on physical fitness.

He has coached at all levels of track and field, swimming, soccer, rugby, basketball, and baseball. He was also the Director of Conditioning for the Chicago White Sox for almost 9 years beginning in 1987. He sees parallels between the evolution of strength and conditioning and the evolution of sleep programs in baseball as both met with early resistance by teams and coaches. Once strength and conditioning gained a foothold in the major leagues, it did not filter down to the minor leagues in any systematic way. Even into the late 1990s there was a lot of old school people running the minor league teams without much enthusiasm for strength and conditioning. It just took time to educate the coaches and get them on board.

In minor leagues the players don't fly across time zones, but have to take 16-hour bus rides after a game. "Sleep was never discussed." Vern Gambetta sees the same systematic resistance with the introduction of sleep programs as was seen in the development of strength and conditioning programs, "teams are more interested in monitoring sleep than modifying behaviours".

The pioneers of strength and conditioning in Major League Baseball and football all came from different backgrounds and brought different systems and techniques. But they were all passionate about strength and conditioning and worked to help the profession evolve over the years. Today strength and conditioning programs are part of the DNA of every professional sport in the world. No professional team can survive without it. A far cry from the late 1970s when such programs met with resistance and suffered from a lack of good research and consistent and effective systems. Now practitioners can obtain university degrees and certifications and can practice within a recognized scope of work. Like all professions, strength and conditioning is still evolving and the research continues. It has been a long few decades, but teams now have full control of athlete strength and conditioning programs during the season and successful athletes prioritize it during the off-season. Epley was right, you can have both strength and conditioning and they are effective together.

The Sleep Evolution

Strength and conditioning programs grew organically within major sports. On the other hand, sleep and the effects of sleep deprivation have largely evolved outside of sports. While sleep "came late to the science party" it has been evolving rapidly in terms of recognizing and treating sleep disorders and the health and safety impacts of sleep deprivation. Further, with rapid developments in technology, generally in the last decade, a consumer market for sleep and health information has appeared. Sleep research and technology did not evolve from sports teams it grew from medical interest and consumer demand. The result is that as teams became interested in controlling sleep as a factor to assist them in improving performance and winning, they had to adapt to existing systems and technologies, not the other way around.

There are many factors that can affect human sleep. Some include, biological sleep disorders (70 – 90 different ones), mental health disorders (about 200 different ones), organic diseases, age, sleep environment, nutrition and timing of meals, napping, stress, temperature, travel, social and environmental factors including lifestyle choices, culture, medications (including prescription drugs, over-the-counter drugs and recreational drugs), etc. Each factor alone or in any combination can affect sleep.

It is not an easy task to diagnose the cause(s) of poor sleep in order to fashion a remedy and the medical field doesn't always help.

Modern medicine has made great advances over the past century, largely as a result of specialization and advanced technology. Every part of our body and mind has a specialist in clinical practice and in research. Even though there is much to learn, we already know a lot about every part of our body and brain including how to identify problems and how to fix them.

Specialists are trained to diagnose and treat medical problems within their own specialty or part of the body. In 1940, 75% of U.S. physicians were general practitioners. By 1970, only about a quarter (25%) of physicians were general practitioners. The obvious trend has been a huge increase in specialists.

What specialists are not generally good at is diagnosing and treating individuals with multiple diseases or conditions, particularly when it involves medical issues outside of their specialty. Estimates show that about 25% of the U.S. suffer with multimorbidities, that is multiple diseases or conditions at the same time. Such patients often have to bounce from specialist to specialist, not always finding the right one or the proper diagnoses. Athletes with sleep issues might very well require multiple specialists to accurately diagnose the cause(s) of any sleep disorder.

Sandeep Jauhar, a cardiologist and author, wrote an opinion piece in *TIME* criticizing the growth in specialists and the lack of coordination in the medical field:

> I remember a 50-year-old patient of my Nigerian colleague who was admitted to the hospital with shortness of breath. During his monthlong *(sic)* stay, which probably cost upward of $100,000, he was seen by a hematologist; an endocrinologist; a kidney specialist; a podiatrist; two cardiologists; a cardiac electrophysiologist; an infectious-disease specialist; a pulmonologist; an ear, nose and throat specialist; a urologist; a gastroenterologist; a neurologist; a nutritionist; a general surgeon; a thoracic surgeon; and a pain specialist. The man underwent 12 procedures, including cardiac catheterization, a pacemaker implant and a bone-marrow biopsy (to investigate only mild anemia). Every day he was in the hospital, his insurance company probably got billed nearly $1,000 for doctor visits alone. When he was discharged (with only minimal improvement in his shortness of breath), follow-up visits were scheduled for him with seven specialists.

Allen Frances, a Professor Emeritus at Duke University, wrote in *HuffPost* in 2016:

> Wherever I travel around the world, I find the same problem – too few GP's, too many specialists. The doctor patient/relationship has lost its healing power. Doctors are too busy doing the wrong things. Patients have been reduced to a collection of lab test results.

> Medical mistakes are far too common because each specialist is treating (or more likely over treating) her

own pet organ. No one is considering the whole patient to organize a global, integrated, safe, and effective treatment plan.

The obvious difficulty is that humans are not a bunch of jigsaw puzzle pieces all taped together, humans are an integrated biological system where each component relies on all the others.

Professional sports teams often employ team physicians. In 2013, the American College of Sports Medicine published a "Consensus Statement" setting out the roles and responsibilities, as well as the education recommended to practice as a team doctor. The document largely deals with the care and management of physical injuries but it does say that it is essential that a team physician, "recognizes other issues that affect athletic performance, including strength and conditioning, nutrition, ergogenic aids, substance abuse, and psychological response to injury."

What is missing entirely from the document is - sleep, travel, and circadian rhythm disruptions, all of which affect the health, safety and performance of athletes.

Sleep is the ultimate "integrated" process and affects all parts of our body and brain. Sleep is not just something we do, it is a critical brain function and is affected by many, many internal and external forces, including mental health.

More than Anxiety

Mental health is an emerging concern in sports. In 2020, the Sports Science Institute (SSI) of the NCAA updated its "Mental

Health Best Practices" manual for universities and student-athletes. It states:

> Insomnia and sleep disorders can be an indicator or risk factor for mental health challenges, and can compromise academic and athletic performance through direct or indirect pathways.

Even in 2018, the SSI had published an "Informational Resource" on anxiety disorders. It stated "that more than 30 percent of student-athletes have experienced overwhelming anxiety." The NCAA sees mental health as an important and common issue in university sports.

In 2017, researchers at the University of Oxford studied 3,755 university students across the U.K. and "found that 'sleep disruption is a driving factor in the occurrence of paranoia, hallucinatory experiences, and other mental health problems in young adults [university students] with an average age of 25.'"

Russell Foster, head of the Oxford Sleep and Circadian Neuroscience Institute, said, "Sleep disruption is a very common feature of mental illness, yet despite its prevalence the clinical relevance is often overlooked, and even when recognized, treatment options are limited."

In 2018, the *BBC* reported on the U.K. government's proposed action plan to deal with mental health for elite athletes:

> Ian Braid, former CEO of the British Athletes' Commission (BAC) and now managing director of Duty of Care in Action (Dociasport), said: "The effects of living in a high performance environment constantly worrying about selection, funding, injury and struggling with their identity on transition can't be underestimated."

"Dealing with athletes' mental health was my biggest challenge at the BAC. I would hope the plan extends to cover a duty of care to coaches, sports support and administrators. The devil will be in the detail and the budget."

In 2018, both Kevin Love, a five-time NBA all-star with the Cleveland Cavaliers, and DeMar DeRozan, a four-time NBA all-star currently with the San Antonio Spurs, stepped into the public spotlight on the issue of mental health. They spoke about their struggles and experiences and encouraged the league and the public to address the issue. This "prompted the National Basketball Players Association to hire Dr. William Parham as its first [D]irector of [M]ental [H]ealth and [W]ellness."

ESPN writer, Jackie MacMullen, wrote on August 2018:

> Yet there remain many obstacles to confront, chief among them the stigma attached to mental health that prompts many players to suffer in silence. The union also insists that mental health treatment be confidential, but some NBA owners, who in some cases are paying their players hundreds of millions of dollars, want access to the files of their "investments." That is not, however, the league's position. "The NBA fully supports protecting the confidentiality of players' mental health information and, accordingly, committed to the players association that any mental health program we undertake would do so," NBA spokesman Mike Bass says.

You cannot have a conversation about sleep without also having a conversation about mental health and you cannot have a conversation about mental health without discussing sleep.

The two are closely linked, they are two sides of the same coin. In 2017, Daniel Freeman, a psychiatrist at Oxford, said, "Sleep problems are a common occurrence in patients with mental health disorders." Further, he said "The traditional view is that disrupted sleep is a symptom" of the mental health disorder but that another perspective is that disturbed sleep is a cause of the mental health disorder. Russell Foster said, "Studies suggest that disrupted sleep such as insomnia could actually help us predict episodes of mental illness and that fixing sleep problems may help treat them."

Mental health issues are common amongst athletes, particularly college and professional athletes. Much like the availability of objective sleep screening and diagnosis using PSG for sleep disorders, there are effective mental health screening programs available. Mental health professionals can use structured clinical interviews to screen for and diagnose mental health issues and provide treatment to athletes. It is much better to discover and treat mental health issues before the athlete burns out or leaves athletics altogether.

Knowledge alone doesn't change behavior.

Amy Bucher

Virtually all teams that have sleep programs begin with athlete education, often called sleep hygiene training. Sleep hygiene is about ensuring the proper sleep environment and lifestyle to create the opportunity to get proper sleep. This includes making sure the sleep environment is comfortable, dark, and quiet. It is often thought that if athletes receive sleep education, they can improve their sleep by making smarter choices. It turns out that is not always true.

In August 2018, Johnpaul Caia and some colleagues from Australia published a paper in *Sleep Health* entitled, "The influence of sleep hygiene education on sleep in professional rugby league athletes". They followed 24 athletes over a 10-week period and monitored their sleep with "wrist activity monitors". They collected baseline sleep data for two weeks on all the athletes. Then 12 of the athletes were given "two 30-minute sleep hygiene education seminars", one week apart. The other 12 received no training. The week after the initial training the first 12 had earlier bedtimes, more time in bed, and increased sleep duration. After the second seminar those athletes had even more time in bed but a reduced sleep efficiency. A month later "sleep behavior was comparable to that observed at baseline". In other words, sleep hygiene education had a short-term effect on sleep behavior. Even after two seminars the athletes were back to their old sleep habits within a month.

Amy Bucher, a health and wellness psychologist, wrote in her article, "The Diminishing Returns of Education for Health Behavior Change" that what is missing is motivation. "Without motivation, people won't use the education to make changes". Athletes are motivated to win. However, knowing that better sleep can improve their performance doesn't automatically help them change their sleep habits. Sleep habits are hard to break. They need motivation and feedback, not just sleep hygiene training.

Athletes are not born with any sleep knowledge and for the most part it is not taught in grade school or high school and rarely in college. One of the challenges is simply time. Medical schools find it hard to add additional classes to an already busy schedule to teach general practitioners about sleep. Similarly, schools, particularly those in the NCAA, also seem reluctant to offer such education.

Under the direction of William Dement, Stanford University found one solution. Beginning in 1971, Dement began offering a course, for credit, open to all students called, "Sleep and Dreams". It proved to be very popular. It provided necessary sleep education to athletes without detracting from practice time. In other words, sleep education for athletes moved from the athletic department to the students' academic program. But this did not necessarily provide the feedback and motivation necessary to change behaviours.

Most athletes understand that they need strength and conditioning. Teams do not need to tell players that. Teams provide equipment, coaching, assessments, goals, monitoring and feedback. Athletes are motivated to get into shape but still require on-going assistance and motivation and even some hand holding to get into shape and to stay in shape.

Consistently obtaining good sleep habits is a process like getting into physical shape, it takes assessments, time, training, technology, feedback, assistance, and effort. Teams would never think of giving athletes a 30-minute talk on getting into shape and expect any real results, but for many teams their entire sleep program consists of a 30 or 60-minute sleep hygiene presentation.

Measuring Sleep

Some teams provide sleep hygiene education as well as measuring the athletes' sleep. The go-to-technology has been actigraphy or sleep watches. Some of this technology is, unfortunately, consumer-grade or "science-ish". The difficulty of course is that teams often do not recognize the limitations of the technology. Are the sleep watches validated against PSG and the target population? What do you do with the data? How does sleep duration, timing and quality affect the core goal of measuring athletic performance?

The decision to use sleep watches for sports teams creates its own set of challenges. Strength and conditioning programs and physical testing occur during the day and normally in team-controlled facilities. Athletes normally sleep at night, at home (except road games). There are privacy issues. Who gets access to the data? With validated sleep watches teams can tell when players are awake and when they are asleep. It can infer a certain lifestyle and possibly even sexual activity. Who interprets the data and who gets access to the data is as important as what decisions are being made based on the data.

Sleep data is usually considered individually identifiable health information and is likely governed by state, provincial and/or federal privacy legislation. The major North American sports leagues all have collective bargaining agreements which can also govern sleep data collection and use. When teams began to use sleep watches to measure players' sleep their unions and the leagues had to scramble. Measuring sleep in this way was simply not contemplated when the agreements were first struck.

In 2015, the National Football Players Association (NFLPA) filed a grievance and wrote to the players:

> It has come to our attention that several Clubs are currently using or have used sensors to monitor players' sleep. Because the use of such technology occurs outside of games and practice, we believe such use violates the Collective Bargaining Agreement. Based on this information, the NFLPA has filed a grievance against

the NFL and all 32 Clubs seeking an order compelling
the NFL and its member clubs to immediately cease and
desist from using unapproved sensor devices on players,
unless or until such use is approved by the NFLPA…

The league and the union eventually agreed to a resolution of
the issue although they have not made it public. What this does
show is that sleep technology was disruptive, and the league and
union had to consider the consequences of sleep measurement,
including player privacy. Not all professional athletes have the
same protections (or any at all).

One of the interesting parallels between strength and
conditioning and sleep is "diagnosis". With strength and
conditioning, individual athletes are fully evaluated before an
individual program is designed. No strength and conditioning
coach would think of giving an athlete a fitness program without
first understanding the baseline strength and conditioning of
the athlete and the athlete's overall health. A program is then
designed to help the player reach certain measurable goals as
an individual and for the position held on the team. The player
is monitored, and progress can be measured objectively. On the
other hand, strength and conditioning coaches often monitor
sleep and try to provide "solutions" to a perceived sleep problem,
without any initial diagnosis or understanding of the complex
reasons the athlete may or may not be sleeping well. For example,
if an athlete's sleep watch shows they are not sleeping well, sleep
education or further monitoring is useless if the athlete has, for
example, unresolved sleep apnea or a mental health issue.

The Sleep Diagnoses

Usually the emphasis for teams is solely on "lifestyle" issues and sleep hygiene as a solution. The question they ask is, what can a player do to improve his/her sleep? The first question should be whether the athlete even has a sleep issue. Perhaps the athlete has perfect sleep health and is sleeping well or perhaps not. Just asking an athlete about his/her sleep is a start, but many people have sleep disorders without even knowing it, and self-reported sleep is not very accurate or helpful in this regard.

There are a number of sleep questionnaires designed to weed out those that may have sleep issues. However, most questionnaires rely on the honesty of the athletes' answers and their own self-awareness of their sleep habits. Questionnaires can screen for some sleep disorders, but they cannot diagnose them. In 2018, the Columbus Blue Jackets in the National Hockey League had all their players screened for sleep disorders using PSG. That is the best way to not only determine if an individual player has a sleep disorder, but also to diagnose the disorder so that the athlete can receive treatment. A 2016 Finish study found that one in four athletes have sleep disorders that are treatable. Athletes, particularly professional athletes, should undergo PSG to determine if they have a sleep disorder and then if they do, have it treated.

How Much Sleep Do Athletes Need?

Athletes are often concerned with how much sleep they need to perform at their best. In 2012 *ESPN* stated, "No line of work requires more sleep than [a] 'professional athlete'". The article continued, stating that tennis star Roger Federer and basketball star LeBron James reported sleeping 12 hours a night and that other stars like Venus Williams, Maria Sharapova, Usain Bolt, and Steve Nash all sleep 10 hours a night. Since those all seem to be self-reported sleep hours it is difficult to determine how much of that is real and how much is hype.

Sleep hours are one factor to consider but so is sleep fragmentation (how broken up the sleep is). The Van Dongen study showed that people could maximize their reaction times by consistently having good sleep for 8 hours. "Subjects allowed an 8 h sleep period per night displayed only minor, non-significant increases in lapses of behavioral alertness over the 14 days." Even if it were possible for those individuals to consistently get 10 or 12 hours of sleep it is not clear if that would make their performance any better, that was not studied. They also noted that there was considerable individual variation in the amount of sleep needed to prevent poor reaction times. The average was 8.16 hours of sleep plus or minus 0.73 hours. Roughly translated into a range of 7.5 to 9 hours of sleep. This means that it is possible for some athletes to maximize their reaction time by having good sleep at night for 7.5 hours, others might take 9 hours.

Those ranges of sleep are for good, uninterrupted sleep. In 2002, Edward Stepanski published a study on the effects of sleep fragmentation on daytime functioning. He concluded, "It is clear from this literature that fragmented sleep is less restorative than consolidated sleep, and leads to sleepiness-related daytime impairment." Similarly, a review on sleep fragmentation literature by Nancy Wesensten and colleagues found that the effects of fragmented sleep impair alertness and performance in the same way sleep deprivation does. In other words, it is not just how long athletes sleep that matters but how broken up their sleep is.

The Team Approach

Sleep programs used in sports have simply not evolved to the point where comprehensive assistance, such as what is provided for physical fitness training, is easily available. While many teams are keen on controlling the important sleep factor, the "sleep file" is often handed to strength and conditioning coaches and usually handled off the corner of their desk. Sleep is not part of their formal professional training and isn't even in the scope of work for their profession. In fact, none of the usual professions employed by teams have embraced sleep as part of their profession.

Strength and condition programs are no longer talked about in terms of teams winning and losing. In the early 1980s when only a handful of football teams had strength programs their win loss records were talked about. That is why many teams jumped on the bandwagon. However, as all teams now have strength and conditioning programs there is no real advantage. Those programs are simply integrated into how teams operate.

Sleep programs are really no different than strength and conditioning programs in that they prepare the athlete to perform at a peak level during games and to assist in their recovery. Maximizing individual sleep can maximize reaction time and the ability to concentrate, all great things during a competition.

However, sleep as a way to enhance performance is new to sports and not always welcomed. Sleep programs do not always fit into the structured schedule of teams as they are often creatures of habit and slaves to tradition. Comments like, "We have always done it this way. Why would we change?" are not unusual. Sleep programs can feel like an uninvited guest at dinner. They can feel awkward.

That said, more and more teams are beginning to embrace sleep programs. As teams embrace sleep, on the same terms as strength and conditioning programs, they will need to address the needs of individual players as well as the team as a whole.

The first step should be to help athletes understand their own individual sleep health. As a starting point, every athlete should undergo proper sleep and mental health screening. Any athletes that have medical issues can then be properly treated.

If teams want to assist their players, they should fully understand how much sleep each player needs and how the time of day affects their reaction time. Teams can then organize their meetings, travel, practices and games (where possible) to provide the best opportunities for the athletes to get the sleep they need. Sleep and fatigue programs need to be based on sleep data from their team, not just generalized data.

Once a team has sleep and circadian rhythm data on their athletes, they can create a team sleep profile. That means superimposing all the data so they can tell when, on average, their team goes to sleep, when they wake up, when they nap, how they sleep on planes or buses, how their sleep varies on game days versus off days, etc. Also, season-to-season data can vary with athlete turnover and schedule changes. Having an up-to-date sleep profile helps teams make more informed decisions about scheduling activities to maximize players' sleep.

The Vancouver Canucks used this method with its active roster players, starting in 2008, to create additional sleep opportunities while travelling. In the National Hockey League it is common for teams to play many back-to-back games on the road. The team might play one night at 7 pm and the next night at 7 pm, but in a different city many hours away. Under NHL rules they are required to travel after the first game. The team always lost sleep after their first evening game as they had to pack up and fly to the next city, often not getting into bed until 1 am or later. There were really only two ways to mitigate the problem.

For the Canucks it meant getting to the next city as quickly as possible so that the players could get into bed faster. It is not uncommon for a team to take a few hours after a game for the players to talk to the media, shower, ride a bike, go through security, take a bus to the airport and then board the plane. The equipment managers have to pack up all the equipment, load it on a truck, go through security, travel to the airport, load the plane and then get on board. The Canucks were able to accomplish all that within an hour after the game was over. This gave their team an hour or more sleep in the next city.

Their secret was convincing the players to hurry up their post-game activities, often foregoing post-game bike workouts. However, the real secret was bringing the equipment managers into the conversation. Ice hockey is a team game and the equipment managers are part of the team. They simply found creative ways to pack up and get the equipment loaded onto the plane faster so that the players could get extra sleep in the next city.

Second, the team tried to go into their first evening game with no sleep debt. Any existing sleep debt would compound the problem of sleep loss for the next game. The time for them to maximize their sleep and reduce any sleep debt was in the days before the first of their back-to-back games.

For example, if their back-to-back games were in Florida and their previous game was in New York they did not travel all night after their New York game. They stayed overnight in New York, thus giving the players more time to sleep and preventing a large sleep debt going into their back-to-back games.

These sorts of time and sleep management options are only really possible to predict and manage if the team understands their team sleep profile.

Of course, not all teams have that luxury. Sometimes budgets do not allow for that. Some teams in other sports have to travel on red-eye flights across the country and play a match that day. This approach puts the athletes at a disadvantage and leagues and teams need to reconsider that approach. Each team, even those in the same league, may have different travel needs and different team sleep profiles. It takes time, effort, and an understanding of the effects of sleep loss and travel to create the necessary sleep opportunities for athletes.

Sleep education is also important. Not on a one-off basis, but constantly reinforced. Part of sleep education involves feedback to the athlete through actigraph data or PVT tests and goal setting. Good sleep habits, like strength and conditioning programs, should occur during both the season and the off-season. It is difficult to get into physical shape at the beginning of a season if strength and conditioning has been neglected during the off-season. The same goes with sleep. Professional athletes should understand that good sleep habits are not something that can be turned on and off easily. Good sleep habits are a lifetime commitment as much as strength and conditioning.

It is often difficult to introduce new concepts, like sleep, to active roster players and have them actually make lifestyle changes and create new habits. It can happen, but it is more difficult. Since sleep education is not provided in public schools, the best place to start introducing sleep education is with the younger and more junior players, often playing in a junior league. This allows the athletes to have the opportunity to acquire good sleep habits early on that could carry on throughout their careers.

In sum, sleep and mental health screening, data collection, and education with constant reinforcement are the key elements to implementing an effective program. Additionally, potions and supplements like melatonin should not be handed out like candy. Melatonin and other "sleep products" should only be used under the direction of a physician and for proper purposes.

Sleep and fatigue is a burgeoning field. Keeping up is a challenge. Teams also need the capacity to understand new research and determine its validity for their team. Popular and well-advertised gadgets and potions may not be valid or appropriate at all. Remember, even things like lie detectors once won awards and were very popular (and are still used) but have little scientific validity.

How Leagues Can Get Involved

While teams can help their athletes by creating sleep opportunities, leagues can also help in this regard since game times and locations are dictated by the leagues. Leagues have to juggle many factors, not least of which are television contracts, availability of sports arenas, and scheduling rules in collective bargaining agreements.

Leagues, generally, do not collect sleep and fatigue data from teams to try to even out the burden between teams, let alone address the important issue of creating realistic sleep opportunities for athletes.

Still, some leagues, like the NBA and the NHL, have taken action. These two leagues added additional days off for athletes during the season thinking the players could use the extra rest. While true, compulsory days off also remove some team travel options such as staying over in a city after a night game and travelling the next day. If that travel day is needed as a compulsory day off, they will have to fly all night to get home so that they can have their day off.

Leagues can also be more responsive to requests from teams for more rest for their players. For example, in Major League Baseball, teams that travel from the West Coast to the East Coast are given a day off to reduce fatigue. Sometimes these days are used by the league to schedule a rain out game. Teams who understand the importance of the day off could ask the league to provide alternative solutions. Simple things can make a difference between winning and losing or making the playoffs or not.

At least one league has proved it can be responsive to a request from a team. The Vancouver Canucks tracked the number of time zone crossings for their team during the season and were able to demonstrate a correlation between time zone crossing and a lack of sleep for their players. After discussing this with the NHL their time zone crossings during road trips eventually started to reduce.

Finally, many leagues employ the officials that umpire or referee games. Officials often have the same (or even worse) travel and sleep issues as athletes. They are also expected to perform at their best during games and their decisions can sometimes have the possibility of determining who wins and who loses. However, leagues do not, for the most part, provide officials with the resources and education to combat sleep and fatigue issues. They should employ the same best practices for sleep and fatigue management that teams are capable of employing.

Not the End

Sleep came late to the science party, but it is catching up. Athletes and teams have the opportunity to create sleep programs that are effective if they treat them like they treat strength and conditioning programs. Easy "solutions" offered through gadgets and potions should be avoided and players and teams should roll up their sleeves. It takes commitment, resources, energy, and education to effectively manage sleep in sports.

In the movie "Moneyball", the general manager of the Oakland A's was explaining his new baseball program to some athletes. How Billie Beane explained it is also applicable to sleep programs:

"This is a process"

"It's a process"

"It's a process."

INCONVENIENT SLEEP

References

Chapter 1 References

Baseball Reference. (2020, May 27). *2018 Toronto Blue Jays Schedule*. Retrieved from https://www.baseball-reference.com/teams/TOR/2018-schedule-scores.shtml

Baseball Reference. (2020, May 27). *Mike Winters*. Retrieved from https://www.baseball-reference.com/bullpen/Mike_Winters

Basketball Reference. (2020, May 24). *2018-19 Toronto Raptors Schedule and Results*. Retrieved from https://www.basketball-reference.com/teams/TOR/2019_games.html

Basketball Reference. (2020, May 27). *Golden State Warriors*. Retrieved from https://www.basketball-reference.com/teams/GSW/

Beaudoin, D., Schulte, O. & Swartz, T.B. (2016). Biased Penalty Calls in the National Hockey League. Statistical Analysis and Data Mining, 9(5), 365-372. Retrieved from http://people.stat.sfu.ca/~tim/papers/penalty.pdf

Belenky, G., Wesensten, N.J., Thorne, D.R., Thomas, M.L., Sing, H.C., Redmond, D.P., Russo, M.B. & Balkin, T.J. (2003). Patterns of performance degradation and restoration during sleep restriction and subsequent recovery: a sleep dose-response study. *Journal of Sleep Research, 12,* 1-12.

Biasiotto, J. (2010, Mar. 16). *15 Surprising Facts About World Class Athletes*. Retrieved from http://agelessadonis.com/15-surprising-facts-about-world-class-athletes/

Birge, M.E. (2014). Sleep Quality and Quantity of Portland State University Intercollegiate Student-Athletes: A Case Study. *Dissertations and Theses*. Paper 1984.

Borow, Z. (2012, Jul. 10). *Tough or Arrogant? Right or Wrong? No Matter What you Think of Umpires, a Week on the Road With Them Proves That They go Above and Beyond the Call.* Retrieved from https://www.espn.com/espn/magazine/archives/news/story?page=magazine-20060814-article20

Boyko, R.H., Boyko, A.R., Boyko, M.G. (2007). Referee bias contributes to home advantage in English Premiership football. *Journal of Sports Sciences, 25(11),* 1185-1194.

Brewer, R. (2020, May 27). *College Football Value Rankings.* Retrieved from https://graphics.wsj.com/table/NCAA_2019

Bridgestock, L. (2019, May 17). *How Much Does it Cost to Study in the US?* Retrieved from https://www.topuniversities.com/student-info/student-finance/how-much-does-it-cost-study-us

Business Wire. (2019, May 14). *Sports - $614 Billion Global Market Opportunities & Strategies to 2022.* Retrieved from https://www.businesswire.com/news/home/20190514005472/en/Sports---614-Billion-Global-Market-Opportunities

Caple, J. (2017, Jan. 11). *Travel will take a toll, but athletes don't have to lose sleep over it.* Retrieved from https://www.espn.com/nba/story/_/id/18415599/travel-take-toll-athletes-lose-sleep-it

Communication with an alumnus of the University of Iowa football program.

Communication with Dennis LaRue.

Communication with Dion Von Molke.

Communication with Kendal Yonomoto.

Communication with Mike Winters.

Desjardins, J. (2017, Aug. 24). *The World's 50 Most Valuable Sports Teams.* Retrieved from https://www.visualcapitalist.com/worlds-50-valuable-sports-teams/

DiGiulio, S. (2016, Jun. 8). *LeBron: If You Can't Score Some Zzs, You Can't Score On The Court.* Retrieved from https://www.huffingtonpost.ca/entry/is-the-nba-finally-learning-how-to-sleep_n_57587446e4b0ced23ca6ce49

Dohmen, T. & Sauermann, J. (2016). Referee Bias. *Journal of Economic Surveys, 30(4),* 679-695.

ESPN. (2007, Sept. 26). *Winters, umpire in Bradley blowup, suspended for season.* Retrieved from https://www.espn.com/mlb/news/story?id=3037237

ESPN. (2018, Mar. 20). *Who's The Highest-Paid Person in Your State?* Retrieved from http://www.espn.com/espn/feature/story/_/id/22454170/highest-paid-state-employees-include-ncaa-coaches-nick-saban-john-calipari-dabo-swinney-bill-self-bob-huggins

REFERENCES

FIFA Magazine. (2007, July). *Big Count: 265 million playing football.* (On file with author).

Fraser, C.G. (1973, Oct. 26). *Now It's All Right to Call an Umpire a Bum.* Retrieved from https://www.nytimes.com/1973/10/26/archives/now-its-all-right-to-call-an-umpire-a-bum.html

Froh, T. (2020, Apr. 5). *A league is born: An oral history of the inaugural MLS match.* Retrieved from https://www.mlssoccer.com/post/2016/04/06/league-born-oral-history-inaugural-mls-match

Holmes, B. (2018, Apr. 10). *How fatigue shaped the season, and what it means for the playoffs.* Retrieved from https://www.espn.com/nba/story/_/id/23094298/how-fatigue-shaped-nba-season-means-playoffs

Holmes, B. (2019, Oct. 14). *'It's the dirty little secret that everybody knows about'.* Retrieved from https://www.espn.com/nba/story/_/id/27767289/dirty-little-secret-everybody-knows-about

Hosick, M.B. (2019, Oct. 16). *DI student-athletes graduate at record high rates.* Retrieved from http://www.ncaa.org/about/resources/media-center/news/di-student-athletes-graduate-record-high-rates

Hursh, S.R., Balkin, T.J., Miller, J.C. & Eddy, D.R. (2004). The Fatigue Avoidance Scheduling Tool: Modeling to Minimize the Effects of Fatigue on Cognitive Performance. *SAE International.* Retrieved from https://www.saftefast.com/downloads/SAE-Hursh-04DHM-14.pdf

Jussim, M. (2020, May 27). *How an NBA Referee Trains to Keep up With the World's Best Athletes.* Retrieved from https://www.mensjournal.com/sports/how-nba-referee-trains-keep-worlds-best-athletes/

Kennedy, J.F. (1961, Apr. 21). *The President's News Conference.* Retrieved from https://www.presidency.ucsb.edu/documents/the-presidents-news-conference-213

Kilgore, A. (2019, Sept. 15). *How the Saints-Rams no-call changed the NFL.* Retrieved from https://www.washingtonpost.com/sports/2019/09/15/how-saints-rams-no-call-changed-nfl/

MacMullan, J. (2018, Aug. 23). *Yelled at, spit on and insulted: Inside the life of an NBA ref.* Retrieved from https://www.espn.com/nba/story/_/id/24391191/nba-mental-health-joey-crawford-stress-referees-jackie-macmullan

Michigan State University. (2011, July 21). *Scholar helps make Major League Baseball umpire schedule a hit.* Retrieved from https://www.sciencedaily.com/releases/2011/07/110720103524.htm#:~:text=One%20improvement%20stemming%20from%20the,in%202008%2C%202009%20or%202010.

Miller, K. (2018, May 3). *How Much Are MLB Umpires Paid?* Retrieved from https://bleacherreport.com/articles/2773321-how-much-are-mlb-umpires-paid

MLB Collective Bargaining Agreement art. V and VII (2017-2021)

MLB. (2020, May 27). *Bios: Mike Winters.* Retrieved from https://www.mlb.com/official-information/umpires/bios

MLS Collective Bargaining Agreement art. 11 (2015-2020)

MLS Players Association. (2020, Jan. 31). *New Tentative CBA Agreement Reached with MLS.* Retrieved from https://mlsplayers.org/resources/cba

N.J.S.A. 2C:11-5 (2002). Retrieved from https://www.njleg.state.nj.us/2002/Bills/S2000/1644_I1.HTM

National Basketball Referees Association. (2020, May 27). *Marc Davis.* Retrieved from https://www.nbra.net/nba-officials/referee-biographies/marc-davis/

NBA Collective Bargaining Agreement art XX (2017-2024).

NCAA Research. (2020, Apr. 8). *Estimated Probability of Competing in College Athletics.* Retrieved from http://www.ncaa.org/about/resources/research/estimated-probability-competing-college-athletics

NCAA Sport Science Institute. *Sleep and Wellness for Collegiate Athletes.* Retrieved from https://ncaaorg.s3.amazonaws.com/ssi/performance/SSI_SleepWellnessFactSheet.pdf

NCAA. (2020, May 25). *Countable Athletically Related Activities.* Retrieved from https://www.ncaa.org/sites/default/files/20-Hour-Rule-Document.pdf

NCAA. (2020, May 25). *History of Division II.* Retrieved from http://www.ncaa.org/about/history-division-ii

NCAA. (2020, May 25). *Play Division III sports.* Retrieved from http://www.ncaa.org/student-athletes/play-division-iii-sports

NCAA. (2020, May 25). *Student-Athletes.* Retrieved from http://www.ncaa.org/student-athletes

NCAA. (2020, May 25). *What is the NCAA?* Retrieved from http://www.ncaa.org/about/resources/media-center/ncaa-101/what-ncaa

NCAA. (2020, May 25). *Where Does the Money Go?* Retrieved from http://www.ncaa.org/about/where-does-money-go

NFL Collective Bargaining Agreement (2011-2020).

NHL Collective Bargaining Agreement art 16 (2012-2022).

Northwestern University, 362 NLRB 167, 1350-1368 (2015).

O'Shaughnessy, L. (2012, Sept. 20). *8 things you should know about sports scholarships.* Retrieved from https://www.cbsnews.com/news/8-things-you-should-know-about-sports-scholarships/

Parker, T. (2019, Oct. 31). *How Much Does the NCAA Make off March Madness?* Retrieved from https://www.investopedia.com/articles/investing/031516/how-much-does-ncaa-make-march-madness.asp

Ruthven, G. (2019, July 1). *Window or aisle, Zlatan? Why MLS teams still fly commercial.* Retrieved from https://www.theguardian.com/football/2019/jul/01/mls-flights-commercial-travel-soccer

Schwab, B. (2015, Aug. 25). *The global players' and athletes' association for professional sport – UNI World Athletes explained.* Retrieved from https://www.lawinsport.com/topics/item/the-global-players-and-athletes-association-for-professional-sport-uni-world-athletes-explained

Scouting the Refs. (2016, Jun. 27). *Referee Dennis LaRue Retires After 26 Seasons.* Retrieved from https://scoutingtherefs.com/2016/06/13515/referee-dennis-larue-retires/

Smith, M.R., Coutts, A.J., Merlini, M., Deprez, D., Lenoir, M. & Marcora, S.M. (2016). Mental Fatigue Impairs Soccer-Specific Physical and Technical Performance. *Medicine & Science in Sports & Exercise, 48(2),* 267-276.

Smith, R.K. (2000). A Brief History of the National Collegiate Athletic Association's Role in Regulating Intercollegiate Athletics. *Marquette Sports Law Review, 11(1),* 5.

Sports Illustrated. (2016, Mar. 1). *WSJ data analysis shows average length of NFL careers decreasing.* Retrieved from https://www.si.com/nfl/2016/03/01/nfl-careers-shortened-two-years-data-analysis

Sportsnet Staff. (2018, June 21). *NHL 2018-19 schedule: Vancouver Canucks.* Retrieved from https://www.sportsnet.ca/hockey/nhl/nhl-2018-19-schedule-vancouver-canucks/

Steinberg, L. (2018, Jul. 28). *What Defines A "Sport"?* Retrieved from https://www.forbes.com/sites/leighsteinberg/2018/07/28/what-defines-a-sport/#799f34ee2d66

University of Notre Dame, Athletics Compliance Office. (2010, Nov. 4). *Countable Hours.* Retrieved from https://www3.nd.edu/~ncaacomp/countable_hours.shtml

USA Today. (2020, May 27). *2019 NCAAF Coaches Salaries.* Retrieved from https://sports.usatoday.com/ncaa/salaries/

Van Dongen, H.P.A., Maislin, G., Mullington, J.M. & Dinges, D.F. (2003). The Cumulative Cost of Additional Wakefulness: Dose-Response Effects on Neurobehavioral Functions and Sleep Physiology From Chronic Sleep Restriction and Total Sleep Deprivation. *Sleep, 26(2),* 117-126.

Vincent, G.E., Onay, Z., Scanlan, A.T., Elsworthy, N., Pitchford, N.W. & Lastella, M. (2020). The Impact of Self-Reported Sleep Quantity on Perceived Decision-Making in Sports Officials during a Competitive Season. *Research Quarterly for Exercise and Sport,* DOI: 10.1080/02701367.2020.1722309

Willis, Z. (2020, Apr. 11). *American Only Has 4 of the Most Profitable Sports Leagues in the World.* Retrieved from https://www.sportscasting.com/america-only-has-4-of-the-most-profitable-sports-leagues-in-the-world/

Wood, R. (2008). *List of Sports – Every sport from around the world.* Retrieved from https://www.topendsports.com/sport/list/index.htm

Wood, R. (2014). *Questionable Sports – Are these really sports?* Retrieved from https://www.topendsports.com/sport/questionable-sports.htm

World Flying Disc Federation. (2020, Jun. 10). *No referee.* Retrieved from http://www.wfdf.org/sports/ddc/62-no-referee

Zarum, D. (2018, Oct. 29). *Toronto Huskies.* Retrieved from https://www.thecanadianencyclopedia.ca/en/article/toronto-huskies

Chapter 2 References

Aserinsky, E. (1987, Nov. 9). *This Week's Citation Classic.* Retrieved from http://garfield.library.upenn.edu/classics1987/A1987K582800001.pdf

Aserinsky, E. (1996). Memories of Famous Neuropsychologists, The Discovery of REM Sleep. *Journal of the History of Neurosciences, 5(3),* 213-227.

Aserinsky, E. & Kleitman, N. (1953). Regularly Occurring Periods of Eye Motility, and Concomitant Phenomena, During Sleep. *Science, 118,* 273-274.

BBC News. (2014, Dec. 9). *Russia's Usmanov to give back Watson's auctioned Nobel medal.* Retrieved from https://www.bbc.com/news/world-europe-30406322

BBC. *The science of sleep.* Retrieved from https://www.bbc.co.uk/science/humanbody/sleep/articles/whatissleep.shtml

Benbadis, S.R. & Rielo, D.A. (2018, May 15). *Normal Sleep EEG.* Retrieved from https://emedicine.medscape.com/article/1140322-overview

Blue, L. (2007, Oct. 19). *The Mortification of James Watson.* Retrieved from http://content.time.com/time/health/article/0,8599,1673952,00.html

Brown, A.P. (2007). J D Bernal: the sage of science. *Journal of Physics: Conference Series, 57,* 61-72.

Brown, C. (2003, Oct.). *The Stubborn Scientist Who Unraveled A Mystery of the Night.* Retrieved from https://www.smithsonianmag.com/science-nature/the-stubborn-scientist-who-unraveled-a-mystery-of-the-night-91514538/

CBS News. (2019, Oct. 5). *Inside the $70 billion industry designed to help you sleep.* Retrieved from https://www.cbsnews.com/news/how-to-sleep-inside-the-70-billion-industry-designed-to-help-you-sleep/

Collop, N.A. (1999). Conundrums in Sleep Medicine. *Chest, 115(3),* 607-608.

Colten, H.R. & Altevogt, B.M. (2006). Preface. In Committee on Sleep Medicine and Research (Ed.). *Sleep Disorders and Sleep Deprivation: An Unmet Public Health Problem.* Washington, D.C.: National Academies Press.

Dement, W.C. (2005). History of Sleep Medicine. *Neurologic Clinics, 23,* 945-965.

Dodson, G. (2002). Dorothy Mary Crowfoot Hodgkin, 12 May 1910 – 29 July 1994. *Biographical Memoirs of Fellows of the Royal Society, 48,* 179-219.

ESPN.com. (2005, May 19). *Backup QB doesn't plan to stop riding.* Retrieved from https://www.espn.com/nfl/news/story?id=2063708

Ferry, G. (2010). The Making of an exceptional scientist. *Nature, 464,* 1268-1270.

Gastfriend, E. (2015, Nov. 5). *90% of All the Scientists That Ever Lived Are Alive Today*. Retrieved from https://futureoflife.org/2015/11/05/90-of-all-the-scientists-that-ever-lived-are-alive-today/

Glynn, J. (2008). Rosalind Franklin: 50 years on. *Notes & Records of the Royal Society, 62,* 253-255.

Grammaticos, P.C. & Diamantis, A. (2008). Useful known and unknown views of the father of modern medicine, Hippocrates and his teacher Democritus. *Hellenic Journal of Nuclear Medicine, 11(1),* 2-4.

Haas, L.F. (2003). Neurological Stamp: Hans Berger (1873-1941), Richard Caton (1842-1926), and electroencephalography. *Journal of Neurology, Neurosurgery and Psychiatry, 74(1),* 9. Retrieved from https://www.ncbi.nlm.nih.gov/pmc/articles/PMC1738204/pdf/v074p00009.pdf

Haba-Rubio, J. & Krieger, J. (2012). Evaluation Instruments for Sleep Disorders: A Brief History of Polysomnography and Sleep Medicine. In Chiang, R.P.-Y. & Kang, S.-C.J. (Ed.). *Introduction to Modern Sleep Technology* (pp. 19-31). Springer Netherlands.

Harvard Medical School, Division of Sleep Medicine. (2007, Dec. 18). *Under the Brain's Control*. Retrieved from http://healthysleep.med.harvard.edu/healthy/science/how/neurophysiology

Harvard Medical School, Division of Sleep Medicine. (2017). *Medical Education*. Retrieved from https://sleep.med.harvard.edu/what-we-do/medical-education

Harvey, A.G. & Tang, N. (2012). (Mis)Perception of Sleep in Insomnia: A puzzle and a resolution. *Psychological Bulletin, 138(1),* 77-101.

Hippocrates. (1868). The Genuine Works of Hippocrates: The Book of Prognostics. *New York Dover (via Digital Hippocrates)*, Part 10. Retrieved from https://www.chlt.org/hippocrates/Adams/page.49.a.php

History.com. (2019, Nov. 8). *German Scientist discovers X-rays*. Retrieved from https://www.history.com/this-day-in-history/german-scientist-discovers-x-rays

Howell, J.D. (2016). Early Clinical Use of the X-Ray. *Transactions of the American Clinical and Climatological Association, 127,* 341-349.

Independent. (2003, Feb. 26). *23 ways that DNA changed the world*. Retrieved from https://www.independent.co.uk/news/science/23-ways-that-dna-changed-the-world-5352712.html

J.D. Bernal. (1958). Dr. Rosalind E. Franklin. *Nature, 182,* 154.

Jeffries, S. (2011, Jan. 29). *The history of sleep science*. Retrieved from https://www.theguardian.com/lifeandstyle/2011/jan/29/history-sleep-science

Kleitman, N. (1939). *Sleep and Wakefulness*. Chicago: University of Chicago Press.

Kram, M. & Pendergast, T. *Reggie White Biography*. Retrieved from https://biography. jrank.org/pages/2548/White-Reggie.html

Lee, J. (2013). Read Francis Crick's $6 Million Letter to Son Describing DNA. *National Geographic*. Retrieved from https://blog.nationalgeographic. org/2013/04/11/read-francis-cricks-6-million-letter-to-son-describing-dna/

Linton, O.W. (1995) Medical Applications of X Rays. *Beam Line, 25(2)*, 25-34. Retrieved from https://www.slac.stanford.edu/pubs/beamline/pdf/95ii.pdf

Maddox, B. (2000, Mar. 5). *The dark lady of DNA?* Retrieved from https://www. theguardian.com/theobserver/2000/mar/05/featuresreview.review

Max, D.T. (2010, May). *The Secrets of Sleep*. Retrieved from https://www. nationalgeographic.com/magazine/2010/05/sleep/

Meixler, E. (2019). Nobel Laureate James Watson Loses Honorary Titles Over 'Reprehensible' Race Comments. *Time*. Retrieved from https://time. com/5501811/james-watson-loses-honors-race-comments/

Michel Jouvet, pioneering sleep scientist – obituary. (2017, Oct. 12). Retrieved from https://www.telegraph.co.uk/obituaries/2017/10/12/michel-jouvet-pioneering-sleep-scientist-obituary/

Millet, D. (2002, Jun. 3). *The origins of EEG*. Retrieved from http://www.bri.ucla.edu/ nha/ishn/ab24-2002.htm

Mindell, J.A., Bartle, A., Wahab, N.A., et al. (2011). Sleep education in medical school curriculum: a glimpse across countries. *Sleep Medicine, 12(9)*, 928-931.

Morrison, A.R. (2013). Coming to Grips with a "New" State of Consciousness: The Study of Rapid-Eye-Movement Sleep in the 1960s. *Journal of the History of the Neurosciences, 22*, 392-407.

Name and Symbol of the Element with Atomic Number 11 (IUPAC Recommendations 2004). *Chemistry International – News Magazine of IUPAC, 27(2)*, 25. DOI: https://doi.org/10.1515/ci.2005.27.2.25b

National Institute of Health. (2007). *Information about Sleep*. Sleep, Sleep Disorders, and Biological Rhythms. Retrieved from https://www.ncbi.nlm.nih.gov/books/ NBK20359/

National Institute of Neurological Disorders and Stroke. (2019, Aug. 13). *Brain Basics: Understanding Sleep*. Retrieved from https://www.ninds.nih.gov/Disorders/ Patient-Caregiver-Education/understanding-Sleep

Nobel Media AB 2020. *The Nobel Prize in Physics 1901*. Retrieved from https://www. nobelprize.org/prizes/physics/1901/summary/

Obituary, Professor J.D. Bernal. *Nature, 235,* 235-236 (1972).

OnThisDay.com (2020, Jun. 1). *Historical Events in 1865.* Retrieved from https://www.onthisday.com/events/date/1865

Portin, P. (2014). The birth and development of the DNA theory of inheritance: sixty years since the discovery of the structure of DNA. *Journal of Genetics, 93(1),* 293-302.

Rogers, A.J., Xia, K., Soe, K., et al. (2017). Obstructive Sleep Apnea among Players in the National Football League: A Scoping Review. *Journal of Sleep Disorders and Therapy, 6(5),* 278.

Röntgen, W.C. (1896). On A New Kind of Rays. *Science, 3(59),* 227-231.

Rubin, J.T. *Newton, Herschel and Ritter: The Discovery of the Spectrum of Light.* Retrieved from https://www.juliantrubin.com/bigten/lightexperiments.html

Sandoiu, A. (2018, Apr. 3). *Insomnia: Why your brain may sleep without even knowing it.* Retrieved from https://www.medicalnewstoday.com/articles/321388

Science Museum. *Wilhelm Conrad Röentgen (1845-1923).* Retrieved from http://broughttolife.sciencemuseum.org.uk/broughttolife/people/wilhelmconrad

SComedy. (2020, Jun. 8). *Quote by Steven Wright.* Retrieved from https://scomedy.com/quotes/10381

Scott, M. (2017, Jan. 1). *Dorothy Hodgkin.* Retrieved from https://www.strangescience.net/hodgkin.htm

Shepard, J.W., Buysse, D.J., Chesson, A.L., et al. (2005). History of the Development of Sleep Medicine in the United States. *Journal of Clinical Sleep Medicine, 1(1),* 61-82.

Spiegel, P.K. (1995). The First Clinical X-Ray Made in America. *ARJ:164,* 241-243.

Stanford University. (1999, Feb. 3). *A Brief History of Sleep Research.* Retrieved from https://web.stanford.edu/~dement/history.html

Stone, J.L. & Hughes, J.R. (2013). Early History of Electroencephalography and Establishment of the American Clinical Neurophysiology Society. *Journal of Clinical Neurophysiology, 30(1),* 28-44.

The Reggie White Sleep Disorders Research & Education Foundation, Inc. Retrieved from http://www.reggiewhitefoundation.org/

The Rosalind Franklin papers. (2019, Dec. 2). Retrieved from https://wellcomelibrary.org/collections/digital-collections/makers-of-modern-genetics/digitised-archives/rosalind-franklin/

Tietz, T. (2018, Mar. 27). *Wilhelm Conrad Röntgen – The Father of Diagnostic Radiology*. Retrieved from http://scihi.org/wilhelm-conrad-roentgen-diagnostic-radiology/

Tobin T.J. (2003). April 25, 1953: Three Papers, Three Lessons. *American Journal of Respiratory and Critical Care Medicine, 167*, 1047-1049.

US Census Bureau. *US Population*. Retrieved from https://www.multpl.com/united-states-population/table/by-year

Waters, H. (2011, Jul. 1). *The First X-ray, 1895*. Retrieved from https://www.the-scientist.com/foundations/the-first-x-ray-1895-42279

Watson, J.D. & Crick, F.H.C. (1953). Molecular Structure of Nucleic Acids. *Nature, 171*, 737-738.

Watson, N.F., Rosen, I.M. & Chervin, R.D. (2017). The Past is Prologue: The Future of Sleep Medicine. *Journal of Clinical Sleep Medicine, 13(1)*, 127-135.

Chapter 3 References

Alder, K. (2009). *The Lie Detectors: The History of an American Obsession.* Nebraska: University of Nebraska Press.

Alder, K. (2020, Mar. 29). *The Lie Detectors, John Larson's California.* Retrieved from http://www.kenalder.com/liedetectors/larson.htm

American Psychological Association. (2004, Aug. 5). *The Truth About Lie Detectors (aka Polygraph Tests).* Retrieved from https://www.apa.org/research/action/polygraph

American Society of Criminology. *Nominations Sought For 2020 August Vollmer Award.* Retrieved from https://www.asc41.com/awards/VollmerAward.html

Argo-A. (2020, Mar. 29). *History of the Polygraph.* Retrieved from https://argo-a.com.ua/eng/history.php

Bartlett, J. (2013, Mar. 12). *Modern-day polygraph dates back to 1921 murder in Pacifica.* Retrieved from https://www.mercurynews.com/2013/03/12/modern-day-polygraph-dates-back-to-1921-murder-in-pacifica/

Beschizza, R. (2008, Feb. 20). *Scam Gadget: Golf Ball Dowser.* Retrieved from https://www.wired.com/2008/02/scam-gadget-gol/

Booth, R. (2013, May 2). *Fake bomb detector conman jailed for 10 years.* Retrieved from https://www.theguardian.com/uk/2013/may/02/fake-bomb-detector-conman-jailed

Brust, A. (2018, Aug. 9). *To tell the truth: What current and hopeful federal employees should know about polygraphs.* Retrieved from https://federalnewsnetwork.com/explainers/2018/08/to-tell-the-truth-how-federal-agencies-use-polygraphs-in-hiring-and-screening/

Buscemi, N., Vandermeer, B., Hooton, N., et al. (2005). The Efficacy and Safety of Exogenous Melatonin for Primary Sleep Disorders. *Journal of General Internal Medicine, 20(12),* 1151-1158.

Byun, J.I., Shin, Y.Y., Chung, S.E. & Shin, W.C. (2018). Safety and Efficacy of Gamma-Aminobutyric Acid from Fermented Rice Germ in Patients with Insomnia Symptoms: A Randomized, Double-Blind Trial. *Journal of Clinical Neurology, 14(3),* 291-295.

CBC, News+Politics. (2013, Dec. 11). *True Story: A Nova Scotia-Born Police Officer Invented The Polygraph, And Today's His Birthday.* Retrieved from https://www.cbc.ca/strombo/news/true-story-a-canadian-invented-the-polygraph-and-todays-his-birthday

CBS News Press Release. (2005, Sept. 29). *For Almost 20 Years, A Husband and Father Was For Almost 20 Years, A Husband and Father was Suspected of Murdering His Wife, But the Murderer was the "BTK" Killer --"48 Hours Mystery".* Retrieved from https://www.viacomcbspressexpress.com/cbs-news/releases/view?id=10900

Cereno, B. (2016, May 9). *Sex, Love, Bondage: The Singular Vision of William Moulton Marston.* Retrieved from https://comicsalliance.com/tribute-william-moulton-marston/

CNN, Law Center. (2003, Dec. 19). *'Green River Killer' sentenced to life in prison.* Retrieved from https://www.cnn.com/2003/LAW/12/18/green.river.sentencing/

Committee to Review the Scientific Evidence on the Polygraph, National Research Council. (2003). *The Polygraph and Lie Detection.* Washington, D.C.: The National Academies Press.

Dinkelspiel, F. (2010, Jan. 27). *Remembering August Vollmer, the Berkeley police chief who created modern policing.* Retrieved from https://www.berkeleyside.com/2010/01/27/remembering-august-vollmer-the-berkeley-police-chief-who-created-modern-policing

Discprofile. (2020, Mar. 25). *William Marston.* Retrieved from https://www.discprofile.com/what-is-disc/william-marston/

Doherty, B. (1996, Nov.). *Box of Dreams.* Retrieved from https://reason.com/1996/11/01/box-of-dreams/

Erland, L.A.E & Saxena, P.K. (2017). Melatonin Natural Health Products and Supplements: Presence of Serotonin and Significant Variability of Melatonin Content. *Journal of Clinical Sleep Medicine, 13(2),* 275-281.

European Food Safety Authority Panel on Dietetic Products, Nutrition and Allergies. (2011). Scientific Opinion on the substantiation of health claims related to L-theanine from *Camellia sinensis* (L.) Kuntze (tea) and improvement of cognitive function, alleviation of psychological stress, maintenance of normal sleep and reduction of menstrual discomfort pursuant to Article 13(1) of Regulation (EC) No 1924/2006. *EFSA Journal, 9(6),* 2238. Retrieved from https://efsa.onlinelibrary.wiley.com/doi/pdf/10.2903/j.efsa.2011.2238

European Food Safety Authority Panel on Dietetic Products, Nutrition and Allergies. (2011). Scientific Opinion on the substantiation of a health claim related to melatonin and reduction of sleep onset latency pursuant to Article 13(1) of Regulation (EC) No 1924/2006. *EFSA Journal, 9(6),* 2241. Retrieved from https://efsa.onlinelibrary.wiley.com/doi/pdf/10.2903/j.efsa.2011.2241

Ferracioli-Oda, E., Qawasmi, A. & Bloch, M.H. (2013). Meta-Analysis: Melatonin for the Treatment of Primary Sleep Disorders. *PLOS One, 8(5),* e63773.

Fisher, J. (2008, Jan. 7). *The Polygraph and the Frye Case*. Retrieved from http://jimfisher.edinboro.edu/forensics/frye.html

Fisher, J. (2008, Jan. 7). *The Polygraph Wars*. Retrieved from http://jimfisher.edinboro.edu/forensics/polywar1.html

French Agency for Food, Environmental and Occupational Health and Safety. (2018, Mar. 8). *ANSES recommends that certain populations avoid the consumption of food supplements containing melatonin*. Retrieved from https://www.anses.fr/en/content/anses-recommends-certain-populations-avoid-consumption-food-supplements-containing-melaton-0

Frye v. United States, 293 F. 1013 (D.C. Cir. 1923).

Gavura, S. (2017, Mar. 9). *Melatonin: What's on the label isn't in the bottle*. Retrieved from https://sciencebasedmedicine.org/melatonin-whats-on-the-label-isnt-in-the-bottle/

Grigg-Damberger, M.M. & Ianakieva, D. (2017). Poor Quality Control of Over-the-Counter Melatonin: What They Say Is Often Not What You Get. *Journal of Clinical Sleep Medicine, 13(2)*, 163-165.

Hawley, C. (2014, Oct. 3). *The story of the fake bomb detectors*. Retrieved from https://www.bbc.com/news/uk-29459896

Hawley, C. & Jones, M. (2010, Jan. 22). *Export ban for useless 'bomb detector'*. Retrieved from http://news.bbc.co.uk/2/hi/programmes/newsnight/8471187.stm

Healthline Media. (2018, Oct. 26). *What Does Gamma Aminobutyric Acid (GABA) Do?* Retrieved from https://www.healthline.com/health/gamma-aminobutyric-acid

Hudson, J. (2010, Nov. 9). *How Many Golf Balls Can Fit In a School Bus?* Retrieved from https://www.theatlantic.com/technology/archive/2010/11/how-many-golf-balls-can-fit-in-a-school-bus/339663/

Iraq-business news. (2013, May 5). *Conman Jailed for Selling Fake Bomb Detectors*. Retrieved from https://www.iraq-businessnews.com/2013/05/05/conman-jailed-for-selling-fake-bomb-detectors/

Jenkins, L. (2018, Feb. 6). *Get Som: The New Solution for NBA Insomniacs*. Retrieved from https://www.si.com/nba/2018/02/06/nuggets-knicks-trey-lyles-blake-griffin-derrick-rose-som-sleep-drink

Kell, G. (2017, Apr. 19). *August Vollmer biography explores famous police chief's UC Berkeley ties*. Retrieved from https://news.berkeley.edu/2017/04/19/august-vollmer-biography-explores-famous-police-chiefs-uc-berkeley-ties/

Kelly, K. (2014, Nov. 8). *The Invention of the Polygraph*. Retrieved from https://americacomesalive.com/2014/11/08/invention-polygraph/

Larson, J.A. (1915). *Thesis: Heredity in finger-prints.* Retrieved from https://open. bu.edu/ds2/stream/?#/documents/105678/page/1

Lepore, J. (2014, Sept. 15). *The Last Amazon, Wonder Woman returns.* Retrieved from https://www.newyorker.com/magazine/2014/09/22/last-amazon

Lockridge, R. (2016, Sept. 21). *Denver Nuggets Strength Coach Steve Hess Explains How Basketball Players Should Eat.* Retrieved from https://www.stack.com/a/ denver-nuggets-strength-coach-steve-hess-explains-how-basketball-players-should-eat

Miller, C. (2010, Nov. 23). *The Invention of Lie Detection: Dr. William Marston And The Creation Of The Lie Detector Test, Frye, & Wonder Woman.* Retrieved from https://lawprofessors.typepad.com/evidenceprof/2010/11/i-was-reading-an-article-about-how-angelina-joliewas-joss-whedons-top-choice-to-play-wonder-womanin-his-first-attempt-at-a-su.html

Minnesota Global, Inc. ... *When You Find Them with the Golf Ball Finder.* Retrieved from http://web.archive.org/web/20030730132205/http://www.mnglobal.com/

National Academy of Sciences. (2003). *The Polygraph and Lie Detection.* Washington, D.C.: The National Academies Press.

National Academy of Sciences. *Public Welfare Medal, August Vollmer 1934.* Retrieved from http://www.nasonline.org/programs/awards/public-welfare-medal.html

National Institutes of Health, Office of Dietary Supplements. (2020, Mar. 24). *Magnesium: Fact Sheet for Health Professionals.* Retrieved from https://ods. od.nih.gov/factsheets/Magnesium-HealthProfessional/

National Institutes of Health, Office of Dietary Supplements. (2020, Feb. 24). *Vitamin B6: Fact Sheet for Health Professionals.* Retrieved from https://ods.od.nih.gov/ factsheets/VitaminB6-HealthProfessional/

National Research Council. (2003). Executive Summary, *The Polygraph and Lie Detection.* (pp. 1-27). Retrieved from https://www.nap.edu/read/10420/chapter/2

National Sleep Foundation. *Melatonin and Sleep.* Retrieved from https://www. sleepfoundation.org/articles/melatonin-and-sleep

Nordland, R. (2009, Nov. 3). *Iraq Swears by Bomb Detector U.S. Sees as Useless.* Retrieved from https://www.nytimes.com/2009/11/04/world/ middleeast/04sensors.html

Nostbakken, J. (2017, Jan. 19). *Lie Detector.* Retrieved from https://ingeniumcanada. org/channel/innovation/lie-detector

NSF International. *About Us.* Retrieved on June 16, 2020, from https://www.nsfsport. com/about-us/

Octagon. (2018, Oct. 16). *Overdose on melatonin and the safety of melatonin.* Retrieved from https://blogs.ubc.ca/rhein/2018/10/16/overdose-on-melatonin-and-the-safety-of-melatonin/

Ono, D. (2005, Aug. 17). *Who is the BTK killer?* Retrieved from http://www.nbcnews.com/id/8929452/ns/us_news-crime_and_courts/t/who-btk-killer/#.XoDM89NKi9Y

Pennington, B. (2010, May 3). *ON PAR; The Burden and Boon of Lost Golf Balls.* Retrieved from https://archive.nytimes.com/query.nytimes.com/gst/fullpage-9500E1DE163FF930A35756C0A9669D8B63.html

Pressler, A. (2019, Mar. 5). *Melatonin: How Much Should I Take for a Good Night's Rest?* Retrieved from https://health.clevelandclinic.org/melatonin-how-much-should-i-take-for-a-good-nights-rest/

Reynolds, C.F. III, Grochocinski, V.J., Monk, T. H., et al. (1992). Concordance Between Habitual Sleep Times and Laboratory Recording Schedules. *Sleep, 15(6),* 571-575.

Robinson, B. (2006, Jan. 7). *Green River Suspect Atypical Serial Killer.* Retrieved from https://abcnews.go.com/US/story?id=90173&page=1

São Paulo Research Foundation. (2018, Dec. 11). *Researchers propose guidelines for the therapeutic use of melatonin.* Retrieved from https://www.eurekalert.org/pub_releases/2018-12/fda-rpg121118.php

SComedy. (2020, Jun. 8). *Quote by Steven Wright.* Retrieved from https://scomedy.com/quotes/10712

Seattle Times. (2011, Feb. 18). *Timeline of the Green River killer case.* Retrieved from https://www.seattletimes.com/seattle-news/timeline-of-the-green-river-killer-case/

Shrivastava, D., Jung, S., Saadat, M., et al. (2014). How to interpret the results of a sleep study. *Journal of Community Hospital Internal Medicine Perspectives, 4(5),* 24983.

Smith, B.H. (2019, Sept. 18). *How Gary Ridgway, 'The Green River Killer,' Was Captured With Nearly 20-Year-Old DNA Evidence.* Retrieved from https://www.oxygen.com/the-dna-of-murder-with-paul-holes/crime-time/green-river-killer-gary-ridgway-dna-capture

Som Sleep. Retrieved on April 5, 2020, from https://getsom.com/

Som Sleep. *Frequently Asked Questions.* Retrieved on April 5, 2020, from https://getsom.com/pages/faq

Som Sleep. (2018, Jun. 19). *Som Sleep Now Available for Purchase at all Central*

Market Locations. Retrieved from https://getsom.com/blogs/press/som-sleep-now-available-for-purchase-at-all-central-market-locations#:~:text=Som%20 Sleep%20is%20an%20NSF,before%20bed%20for%20better%20sleep.

Som Sleep. *Som Sleep Original 12 Pack, Supplement Facts.* Retrieved on April 5, 2020, from https://getsom.com/products/som-sleep-original-12-pack

Tampa Bay Times. (2005, Sept. 15). *High-tech drug, gun detector may be fraud.* Retrieved from https://www.tampabay.com/archive/1996/01/27/high-tech-drug-gun-detector-may-be-fraud/

The Scotsman, The Newsroom. (2004, Mar. 29). *BTK Strangler resurfaces after 25 years.* Retrieved from https://www.scotsman.com/news/world/btk-strangler-resurfaces-after-25-years-2512909

United States Golf Association. (2020, Mar. 17). *Major Change: Time for Search Before a Ball is Lost.* Retrieved from https://www.usga.org/content/usga/home-page/rules-hub/rules-modernization/major-changes/reduced-time-for-search-before-a-ball-is-lost.html

United States v. Quadro Corp., 928 F. Supp. 688 (E.D. Tex. 1996)

United States v. Scheffer, 523 U.S. 303 (1998)

University of California, Berkeley. (2005, Feb. 7). *Melatonin shrinks bird gonads. What does the popular supplement do in humans?* Retrieved from https://www.eurekalert.org/pub_releases/2005-02/uoc--msb020405.php

University of Washington. *August Vollmer Award.* Retrieved from https://www.washington.edu/research/or/honors-and-awards/august-vollmer-award/

Web Developers Notes. (2020, Mar. 21). *John Augustus Larson Death Anniversary.* Retrieved from https://www.webdevelopersnotes.com/john-augustus-larson-death-anniversary

Chapter 4 References

American Chemical Society. (2019, Apr. 1). *'Smart' pajamas could monitor and help improve sleep.* Retrieved from https://www.sciencedaily.com/releases/2019/04/190401075143.htm

Ancoli-Israel, S., Cole, R., Alessi, C., et al. (2003). The Role of Actigraphy in the Study of Sleep and Circadian Rhythms. *Sleep, 26(3),* 342-355.

Boyle, R.H. (2020, May 31). *Sports of the Founding Fathers.* Retrieved from https://vault.si.com/vault/1955/07/04/sports-of-the-founding-fathers

Centers for Disease Control and Prevention. (2016, Feb. 18). *1 in 3 adults don't get enough sleep.* Retrieved from https://www.cdc.gov/media/releases/2016/p0215-enough-sleep.html

Communication with Daniel Kripke.

Crunchbase Inc. (2020, May 31). *OURA.* Retrieved from https://www.crunchbase.com/organization/%C5%8Cura#section-overview

Daniel Frederick Kripke, M.D. (2014, Jan.) *Curriculum Vitae.* Retrieved from https://srbr.org/wp-content/uploads/2016/01/KripkeDF_CV.pdf

De Dreem, A. (2020, May 31). *FAQs: pink noises.* Retrieved from https://support.dreem.com/hc/en-gb/articles/360018132971-FAQs-pink-noises

Demand for Jury Trial, *Batungbacal v. Power Balance LLC.* No. SACV11-00018. U.S. District Court, Central District of California, Western Division. (Jan 4, 2011).

de Zambotti, M., Rosas, L., Colrain, I.M., et al. (2017). The Sleep of the Ring: Comparison of the OURASleep Tracker Against Polysomnography. *Behavioral Sleep Medicine.* DOI: 10.1080/15402002.2017.1300587

Division of Sleep Medicine at Harvard Medical School. (2007, Dec. 18). *Natural Patterns of Sleep.* Retrieved from http://healthysleep.med.harvard.edu/healthy/science/what/sleep-patterns-rem-nrem

Dreem. (2016, Mar. 11). *A scientific overview of Rhythm's technology: the Dreem headband. (On file with author)*

Dreem. (2019, Mar.) *Whitepaper. (On file with author)*

Duking, P., Hotho, A., Holmberg, H.C., Fuss, F.K. & Sperlich, B. (2016). Comparison of Non-Invasive Individual Monitoring of the Training and Health of Athletes with Commercially Available Wearable Technologies. *Frontiers in Physiology, 7,* 71.

Ellen. (2014, Aug. 13). *The Evolution of the Pedometer.* Retrieved from https://walkertracker.com/blog/the-evolution-of-the-pedometer/

Ewalt, D.M. (2006, Nov. 13). *Nintendo's Wii Is A Revolution.* Retrieved from https://www.forbes.com/2006/11/13/wii-review-ps3-tech-media-cx_de_1113wii.html#3bc2a3b175bb

Fitbit Inc. (2020, May 31). *How do I track my health and fitness goals with the Fitbit app?* Retrieved from https://help.fitbit.com/articles/en_US/Help_article/1955

Fitbit Inc. (2020, May 30). *Investor FAQ.* Retrieved from https://investor.fitbit.com/overview/investor-faq/default.aspx

Form B1, *Power Balance, LLC.* No. 8:11-bk-25982-TA. United States Bankruptcy Court, Central District of California. (Nov. 18, 2011).

Fusfeld, A. (2011, Jan. 11). *Sacramento Kings To Name Their Arena After Those Power Balance Bracelets That Don't Do Anything.* Retrieved from https://www.businessinsider.com/sacramento-kings-arco-arena-renamed-power-balance-pavilion

Goodreads, Inc. (2020, May 30). *Steven Wright Quotable Quote.* Retrieved from https://www.goodreads.com/quotes/121065-i-intend-to-live-forever-so-far-so-good

Hannu, K. & Heli, K. (2018). The HRV of the Ring – Comparison of nocturnal HR and HRV between the OURA ring and ECG. *Sleep 41(suppl 1),* A120. Retrieved from https://doi.org/10.1093/sleep/zsy061.311

Hartford, T. (2011, Nov. 29). *Power Balance Files for Bankruptcy Protection Under Lawsuit Pressure…* Retrieved from https://sgbonline.com/power-balance-files-for-bankruptcy-protection-under-lawsuit-pressure/

Hilditch, C.J. & McHill, A.W. (2019). Sleep inertia: current insights. *Nature and Science of Sleep, 11,* 155-165.

History.com. (2020, May 31). *Germany annexes Austria.* Retrieved from https://www.history.com/this-day-in-history/germany-annexes-austria

History.com. (2020, Jan. 31). *Thomas Jefferson.* Retrieved from https://www.history.com/topics/us-presidents/thomas-jefferson

Hockey Reference. (2020, May 30). *2009-10 NHL Summary.* Retrieved from https://www.hockey-reference.com/leagues/NHL_2010.html

Hockey Reference. (2020, May 31). *Philadelphia Flyers.* Retrieved from https://www.hockey-reference.com/teams/PHI/history.html

Ioannou, K., Ignaszewski, M. & Macdonald, I. (2014). Ambulatory electrocardiography: The contribution of Normal Jefferis Holter. British Columbia Medical Journal, 56(2), 86-89.

Khosla, S., Deak, M.C., Gault, D., et al. (2018). Consumer Sleep Technology: An American Academy of Sleep Medicine Position Statement. *Journal of Clinical Sleep Medicine, 14(5),* 877-880.

Kinnunen, H. (2016, Feb. 9). *Sleep Lab Validation of a Wellness Ring in Detecting Sleep Patterns Based on Photoplethysmogram, Actigraphy and Body Temperature.* Retrieved from https://ouraring.com/wp-content/uploads/2017/08/Validity-of-the-OURA-Ring-in-determining-Sleep-Quantity-and-Quality-2016.pdf

Kosecki, D. (2018, Sept. 19). *REM, Light, Deep: How Much of Each Stage of Sleep Are You Getting?* Retrieved from https://blog.fitbit.com/sleep-stages-explained/

Leavitt, J. (2019, Oct. 10) *How Much Deep, Light, and REM Sleep Do You Need?* Retrieved from https://www.healthline.com/health/how-much-deep-sleep-do-you-need#sleep-deprivation

Liu, S. (2019, Oct. 17). *Fitbit – Statistics & Facts.* Retrieved from https://www.statista.com/topics/2595/fitbit/

Loeb, S. (2017, Feb. 21). When Fitbit was young: the early years. Retrieved from https://vator.tv/news/2017-02-21-when-fitbit-was-young-the-early-years

MacMahon, T. (2012, Nov. 26). *Mark Cuban rips NBA over bracelets.* Retrieved from https://www.espn.com/dallas/nba/story/_/id/8677068/mark-cuban-dallas-mavericks-blasts-nba-scam-bracelet-deal

Marcin, A. (2018, Dec. 7). *Are You a Healthy Weight? Weight Ranges by Height and Sex.* Retrieved from https://www.healthline.com/health/how-much-should-i-weigh

Medina, M. (2011, Nov. 21). *Power Balance Hit with $57 Million Settlement; Declares Bankruptcy.* Retrieved from https://sacramento.cbslocal.com/2011/11/21/report-power-balance-hit-with-57m-settlement-plans-to-declare-bankruptcy/

Montgomery-Downs, H.E., Insana, S.P. & Bond, J.A. (2012). Movement toward a novel activity monitoring device. *Sleep and Breathing, 16(3),* 913-17.

Morgenthaler, T., Alessi, C., Friedman, L., et al. (2007). Practice Parameters for the Use of Actigraphy in the Assessment of Sleep and Sleep Disorders: An Update for 2007. *Sleep, 30(4),* 519-529.

Nunez, K. (2019, June 21). *What is Pink Noise and How Does It Compare with Other Sonic Hues?* Retrieved from https://www.healthline.com/health/pink-noise-sleep

Order Re Motion to Dismiss, *Brickman, et al. v. Fitbit, Inc.,* No. 3:15-cv-02077, U.S. District Court for the Northern District of California. (July 15, 2016).

Pedometer Reviews – Each Step You Take. (2020, May 30). *Who Invented the Pedometer?* Retrieved from http://eachstepyoutake.com/who-invented-the-pedometer/

Philadelphia Flyers. (2010, June 17). *Philadelphia Flyers 2009-10 Season Recap*. Retrieved from https://www.nhl.com/flyers/news/philadelphia-flyers-2009-10-season-recap/c-531917

Power Balance Wristbands. (2020, May 30). *Posts tagged 'Black'*. Retrieved from https://powerbalancewristbands.wordpress.com/tag/black/

Power Balance. (2020, May 30). *FAQ*. Retrieved from http://www.powerbalance.com/default/faq

Power Balance. (2020, May 30). *Power Balance Wristbands: Corrective Advertisement*. Retrieved from https://www.flickr.com/photos/9076786@N07/5325239980/

Power Balance. (2020, May 30). *Report a Fake*. Retrieved from http://www.powerbalance.com/report-a-fake

Roenigk, A. (2010, Oct. 15). *The power of belief*. Retrieved from http://sports.espn.go.com/espn/news/story?id=5660039

Rovell, D. (2010, Dec. 29). *CNBC's Sports Product of the Year: Power Balance*. Retrieved from https://www.cnbc.com/id/40842683

Russo, K., Goparaju, B. & Bianchi, M. T. (2015). Consumer sleep monitors: is there a baby in the bathwater? *Nature and Science of Sleep, 7,* 147-157.

Sadeh, A. (2011). The role and validity of actigraphy in sleep medicine: An update. *Sleep Medicine Reveiws, 15,* 259-267.

Silbert, S. (2019, July 8). All the Things You Can Track With Wearables. Retrieved from https://www.lifewire.com/what-wearables-can-track-4121040

Silverberg, D. (2018, Apr. 16). *Can Fitbit get itself back into shape?* Retrieved from https://www.bbc.com/news/business-43632634

SleepTrackers.io. (2020, May 31). *Sleep Trackers: Bedroom*. Retrieved from https://sleeptrackers.io/sleep-trackers/bedroom/

Smith, M.T., McCrae, C.S., Cheung, J., et al. (2018). Use of Actigraphy for the Evaluation of Sleep Disorders and Circadian Rhythm Sleep-Wake Disorders: An American Academy of Sleep Medicine Clinical Practice Guideline. Journal of Clinical Sleep Medicine, 14(7), 1231-1237.

Spector, D. (2011, Nov. 21). *Power Balance Will Keep Making Wristbands Despite Bankruptcy And Massive Fraud Lawsuit*. Retrieved from https://www.businessinsider.com/power-balance-bracelets-2011-10

Thorpy, M. & Ancoli-Israel, S. (2004). In Memoriam: William Gruen, July 19, 1919 – October 16, 2004. *Sleep, 27(8),* 1450.

Thorpy, M. & Ancoli-Israel, S. (2005). In Memoriam: William Gruen, July 19, 1919 – October 16, 2004. *Sleep Medicine, 6,* 185-186.

Top Class Actions. (2019, Feb. 28). *Fitbit Sleep Tracker Class Action Settlement.* Retrieved from https://topclassactions.com/lawsuit-settlements/closed-settlements/882456-fitbit-sleep-tracker-class-action-settlement/

Underdown, J. (2012). Special Report: Power Balance Bracelets A Bust in Tests. *Skeptical Inquirer, 36,* 1. Retrieved from https://skepticalinquirer.org/2012/01/power-balance-bracelets-a-bust-in-tests/

University of California, San Diego. *UCSD Profiles: Daniel Kripke.* Retrieved from https://profiles.ucsd.edu/daniel.kripke

United States Courts. (2020, May 31). *Chapter 11 – Bankruptcy Basics.* Retrieved from https://www.uscourts.gov/services-forms/bankruptcy/bankruptcy-basics/chapter-11-bankruptcy-basics

William (Bill) Gruen Obituary. (2004, Oct. 18). Retrieved from https://www.legacy.com/obituaries/nytimes/obituary.aspx?n=william-gruen-bill&pid=2725240

Chapter 5 References

American Academy of Sleep Medicine. (2007, Oct. 16). *People Overestimate Their Self-reported Sleep Times Compared To Measures By A Sleep Test.* Retrieved from https://www.sciencedaily.com/releases/2007/10/071015081530.htm

Aschwanden, C. & Nguyen, M. (2018, May 16). *How Shoddy Statistics Found A Home In Sports Research.* Retrieved from https://fivethirtyeight.com/features/how-shoddy-statistics-found-a-home-in-sports-research/

Bohannon, J. (2013, Oct. 4). *Who's Afraid of Peer Review?* Retrieved from https://science.sciencemag.org/content/342/6154/60

Bohannon, J. (2015, May 27). *I Fooled Millions Into Thinking Chocolate Helps Weight Loss. Here's How.* Retrieved from https://io9.gizmodo.com/i-fooled-millions-into-thinking-chocolate-helps-weight-1707251800

Bohannon, J., Koch, D., Homm, P. & Driehaus, A. (2015). Chocolate with high Cocoa content as a weight-loss accelerator. *International Archives of Medicine, 8(1),* 55. Retrieved from http://melaniestefan.net/Bohannon.pdf

Boon, S. (2017, Jan. 7). *21st Century Science Overload.* Retrieved from http://blog.cdnsciencepub.com/21st-century-science-overload/

Brown, H. (1972). History and the learned journal. *Journal of the History of Ideas, 33(3),* 365-377.

DePaulo, P. (2000, Dec.). *Sample size for qualitative research.* Retrieved from https://www.quirks.com/articles/sample-size-for-qualitative-research

Division of Investigative Oversight, National Institutes of Health. *Findings of Scientific Misconduct: NOT-OD-09-082.* Retrieved from https://grants.nih.gov/grants/guide/notice-files/not-od-09-082.html

Duffy, B. (2016, Dec. 13). *The Importance of Sleep in Athletics: Training, Performance and Injury.* Retrieved from https://www.aastweb.org/blog/the-importance-of-sleep-in-athletics-training-performance-and-injury

Fanelli, D. (2009). How Many Scientists Fabricate and Falsify Research? A Systematic Review and Meta-Analysis of Survey Data. *PLOS One, 4(5),* e5738.

Gastfriend, E. (2015, Nov. 5). *90% of all the Scientists who Ever Lived are Alive Today.* Retrieved from http://www.harvardea.org/blog/2015/11/19/32sq17quhcminti4073fqmzp98yrll

Girschik, J., Fritschi, L., Heyworth, J. & Waters, F. (2012). Validation of Self-Reported Sleep Against Actigraphy. *Journal of Epidemiology, 22(5),* 462-468.

Godlee, F., Gale, C.R. & Martyn, C.N. (1998). Effect on the Quality of Peer Review of Blinding Reviewers and Asking Them to Sign Their Reports. *Journal of the American Medical Association. 280(3)*, 237-240.

Harvard University, Program in Ethics & Health. *John Bohannon*. Retrieved from https://web.archive.org/web/20171015220935/http://peh.harvard.edu/people/bohannon.html

Harvard-Westlake School. (2020, May 18). *Teams*. Retrieved from https://www.hw.com/athletics/Teams

Horvath, J. (2013, Dec. 4). *The Replication Myth: Shedding Light on One of Science's Dirty Little Secrets*. Retrieved from https://blogs.scientificamerican.com/guest-blog/the-replication-myth-shedding-light-on-one-of-sciencee28099s-dirty-little-secrets/

Hughes, L. (2014). The State of Science and Unreliable Research. *Scottish Universities Medical Journal, 3(supp1)*, s6-s11.

Jinha, A.E. (2010). Article 50 million: an estimate of the number of scholarly articles in existence. *Learned Publishing, 23(3)*, 258-263.

Kolata, G. (2018, Oct. 29). *He Promised to Restore Damaged Hearts. Harvard Says His Lab Fabricated Research*. Retrieved from https://www.nytimes.com/2018/10/29/health/dr-piero-anversa-harvard-retraction.html

Levine, D.R. (2013, Oct. 6). *In Study, Open Access Science Journals Accept Fake Papers*. Retrieved from https://www.thecrimson.com/article/2013/10/16/study-science-journals-fake-research/

Mannix, L. (2019, Nov. 15). *Cold water poured on scientific studies based on 'statistical cult'*. Retrieved from https://www.smh.com.au/national/cold-water-poured-on-scientific-studies-based-on-statistical-cult-20191108-p538t6.html

Markovich, A.N., Gendron, M.A. & Corkum, P.V. (2015). Validating the Children's Sleep Habits Questionnaire against polysomnography and actigraphy in school-aged children. *Frontiers in Psychiatry, 5,* 188. Retrieved from https://www.frontiersin.org/articles/10.3389/fpsyt.2014.00188/full

Martin, G. (2020, Jun. 8). *There are three kinds of lies . . .* Retrieved from https://www.phrases.org.uk/meanings/lies-damned-lies-and-statistics.html

Milewski, M.D., Skaggs, D.L., Bishop, G.A., Pace, J.L., Ibrahim, D.A., Wren, T.A.L. & Barzdukas, A. (2014). Chronic Lack of Sleep is Associated With Increased Sports Injuries in Adolescent Athletes. *Journal of Pediatric Orthopedics, 34(2)*, 129-133.

Miller, H. & Young, S.S. (2017, Dec. 13). *Viewpoint: Why so many scientific studies are flawed and poorly understood*. Retrieved from https://geneticliteracyproject.org/2017/12/13/viewpoint-many-scientific-studies-flawed-poorly-understood/

Motulsky, H.J. (2014). Common Misconceptions about Data Analysis and Statistics. *The Journal of Pharmacology and Experimental Therapeutics, 351(1),* 200-205.

National Institutes of Health. (2001, June 17). *Stem Cell Information, Chapter 4: The Adult Stem Cell.* Retrieved from https://stemcells.nih.gov/info/2001report/chapter4.htm

Nayak. B.K. (2010). Understanding the relevance of sample size calculation. *Indian Journal of Ophthalmology, 58(6),* 469-470.

Neale, T. (2012, Oct. 21). *Sleepy Athletes More Likely to be Injured.* Retrieved from https://www.medpagetoday.com/meetingcoverage/aap/35466

Norman, J. (2020, Mar. 8). *Journal des sçavans: The First Scientific Journal Begins Publication.* Retrieved from http://www.historyofinformation.com/detail.php?entryid=2661

Pepper, M.S. (2015, Aug. 19). *A beginner's guide to understanding stem cells.* Retrieved from https://theconversation.com/a-beginners-guide-to-understanding-stem-cells-45502

Press Gazette. (2005, Feb. 11). *Godlee is made BMJ's first woman editor.* Retrieved from https://www.pressgazette.co.uk/godlee-is-made-bmjs-first-woman-editor/

Science Buddies. *Variables in Your Science Fair Project.* Retrieved from https://www.sciencebuddies.org/science-fair-projects/science-fair/variables

Scimago Lab. (2020, May 17). *Journal Rankings on Sports Science.* Retrieved from https://www.scimagojr.com/journalrank.php?category=3699

Spinak, E. & Packer, A.L. (2015, Mar. 5). *350 years of scientific publications: from the "Journal des Sçavans" and Philosophical Transactions to SciELO.* Retrieved from https://blog.scielo.org/en/2015/03/05/350-years-of-scientific-publication-from-the-journal-des-scavans-and-philosophical-transactions-to-scielo/#.Xks7oxNKjBI

Suster, M. (2010, Feb. 17). *73.6% Of All Statistics Are Made Up.* Retrieved from https://www.businessinsider.com/736-of-all-statistics-are-made-up-2010-2

Sutherland, W.J., Spiegelhalter, D. & Burgman, M.A. (2013). Twenty tips for interpreting scientific claims. *Nature, 503,* 335-337.

The Economist. (2013, Oct. 21). *How science goes wrong.* Retrieved from https://www.economist.com/leaders/2013/10/21/how-science-goes-wrong

United Nations Educational, Scientific and Cultural Organization. (2020, May 17). *UNESCO Science Report.* Retrieved from https://en.unesco.org/unesco_science_report/figures

University of Pennsylvania School of Arts & Science, Department of Biology. (2020,

Mar. 24). *David S. Roos.* Retrieved from https://live-sas-bio.pantheon.sas.upenn.edu/people/david-s-roos

Victoria University. *Dr William Hopkins.* Retrieved from https://www.vu.edu.au/research/william-hopkins

Welsh, A. & Knight, E. (2014, Aug. 22). *"Magnitude based-inference": A statistical review.* Retrieved from https://www.clearinghouseforsport.gov.au/international/videos/smart_talk_seminar_series/2014_smart_talk_seminar_series/magnitude_based-inference_a_statistical_review

World Health Organization. (2017, May 17.) *Cardiovascular diseases (CVDs), Key Facts.* Retrieved from https://www.who.int/news-room/fact-sheets/detail/cardio-vascular-diseases-(cvds)

Chapter 6 References

Aeschbach, D., Sher, L., Postolache, T.T., Matthews, J.R., Jackson, M.A. & Wehr, T.A. (2003). A Longer Biological Night in Long Sleepers Than in Short Sleepers. *The Journal of Clinical Endocrinology & Metabolism, 88(1)*, 26-30.

Alvarez, J. (2019, Aug. 28). *After 10-Year Search, Scientists Find Second 'Short Sleep' Gene*. Retrieved from https://www.ucsf.edu/news/2019/08/415261/after-10-year-search-scientists-find-second-short-sleep-gene

Belenky, G., Wesensten, N.J., Thorne, D.R., Thomas, M.L., Sing, H.C., Redmond, D.P., Russo, M.B. & Balkin, T.J. (2003). Patterns of performance degradation and restoration during sleep restriction and subsequent recovery: a sleep dose-response study. *Journal of Sleep Research, 12*, 1-12.

Chaput, J.P., Dutil, C. & Sampasa-Kanyinga, H. (2018). Sleeping hours: what is the ideal number and how does age impact this? *Nature and Science of Sleep, 10*, 421-430.

Communication with Cheri Mah.

Dashti, H.S., Jones, S.E., Wood, A.R. et al. (2019). Genome-wide association study identifies genetic loci for self-reported habitual sleep duration supported by accelerometer-derived estimates. *Nature Communications 10*, 1100. Retrieved from https://www.nature.com/articles/s41467-019-08917-4

Dawson, D. & Reid, K. (1997). Fatigue, alcohol and performance impairment. *Nature, 338*, 235.

Grandner, M.A. & Drummond, S.P.A. (2007). Who Are the Long Sleepers? Towards an Understanding of the Mortality Relationship. *Sleep Medicine Review, 11(5)*, 341-360.

Harbison, S.T., Serrano Negron, Y.L., Hansen, N.F. & Lobell, A.S. (2017). Selection for long and short sleep duration in *Drosophilia melanogaster* reveals the complex genetic network underlying natural variation in sleep. *PLOS Genetics, 13(12)*, e1007098.

Harmon, K. (2009, Aug. 13). *Rare Genetic Mutation Lets Some People Function with Less Sleep*. Retrieved from https://www.scientificamerican.com/article/genetic-mutation-sleep-less/

Harvard Medical School, Division of Sleep Medicine. (2007, Dec. 18). *Sleep, Learning, and Memory*. Retrieved from http://healthysleep.med.harvard.edu/healthy/matters/benefits-of-sleep/learning-memory

Harvard Medical School, Division of Sleep Medicine. (2020, May 2). *Consequences of Insufficient Sleep*. Retrieved from http://healthysleep.med.harvard.edu/healthy/matters/consequences

Hayashi, M., Watanabe, M. & Hori, T. (1999). The effects of a 20 min nap in the mid-afternoon on mood, performance and EEG activity. *Clinical Neurophysiology, 110(2)*, 272-279.

Hayashi, M., Ito, S. & Hori, T. (1999). The effects of a 20-min nap at noon on sleepiness, performance and EEG activity. *International Journal of Psychophysiology, 32(2)*, 173-180.

He, Y., Jones, C.R., Fujiki, N. et al. (2009). The Transcriptional Repressor DEC2 Regulates Sleep Length in Mammals. *Science, 325(5942)*, 866-870.

Hilditch, C.J. & McHill, A.W. (2019). Sleep inertia: current insights. *Nature and Science of Sleep, 11*, 155-165.

Jike, M., Itani, O., Watanabe, N., Buysse, D.J., & Kaneita, Y. (2018). Long sleep duration and health outcomes: A systematic review, meta-analysis and meta-regression. *Sleep Medicine Reviews, 39*, 25-36.

Johns Hopkins Medicine. (2020, Apr. 22). *Oversleeping: Bad for Your Health?* Retrieved from https://www.hopkinsmedicine.org/health/wellness-and-prevention/oversleeping-bad-for-your-health

Lederhouse, C. (2017, Apr. 10). *Short sleepers and long sleepers*. Retrieved from http://sleepeducation.org/news/2017/04/10/short-sleepers-and-long-sleepers

Lovato, N. & Lack, L. (2010). The effects of napping on cognitive functioning. In G.A. Kerkhof & P.A. Van Dongen (Eds.). *Progress in Brain Research* (Vol. 185, pp. 155-166). Amsterdam, N.L.: Elsevier B.V.

Mah, C.D., Mah, K.E., Kezirian, E.J. & Dement, W.C. (2011). The Effects of Sleep Extension on the Athletic Performance of Collegiate Basketball Players. *Sleep, 34(7)*, 943-950.

Mah, C.D., Kezirian, E.J., Marcello, B.M. & Dement, W.C. (2018). Poor sleep quality and insufficient sleep of a collegiate student-athlete population. *Sleep Health, 4(3)*, 251-257.

McDevitt, E.A., et al. (2018). The impact of frequent napping and nap practice on sleep-dependent memory in humans. *Scientific Reports, 8*, 15053.

Miller, N.L., Shattuck, L.G., Matsangas, P. & Dyche, J. (2008). Sleep and Academic Performance in U.S. Military Training and Education Programs. *Mind, Brain, and Education, 2(1)*, 29-33.

REFERENCES

National Institutes of Health. (2017, Dec. 14). *To sleep or not: researchers explore complex genetic network behind sleep duration.* Retrieved from https://www.nih.gov/news-events/news-releases/sleep-or-not-researchers-explore-complex-genetic-network-behind-sleep-duration

National Sleep Foundation. *White Paper: How Much Sleep Do Adults Need?* Retrieved from https://www.sleepfoundation.org/professionals/whitepapers-and-position-statements/white-paper-how-much-sleep-do-adults-need

National Sleep Foundation. *How Much Sleep Do We Really Need?* Retrieved from https://www.sleepfoundation.org/articles/how-much-sleep-do-we-really-need

Neuroscience News & Research. (2017, Dec. 15). *Scientists Probe Genetics of Long and Short Sleepers.* Retrieved from https://www.technologynetworks.com/neuroscience/news/scientists-probe-genetics-of-long-and-short-sleepers-295247

Pellegrino, R., et al. (2014). A Novel BHLHE41 Variant is Associated with Short Sleep and Resistance to Sleep Deprivation in Humans. *Sleep 37(8),* 1327-1336(B).

Thorpy, M.J. (2012). Classification of Sleep Disorders. *Neurotherapeutics, 9(4),* 687-701.

Van Dongen, H.P.A. & Dinges, D.F. (2005). Sleep, Circadian Rhythms, and Psychomotor Vigilance. *Clinics in Sports Medicine, 24,* 237-249.

Van Dongen, H.P.A., Maislin, G., Mullington, J.M. & Dinges, D.F. (2003). The Cumulative Cost of Additional Wakefulness: Dose-Response Effects on Neurobehavioral Functions and Sleep Physiology From Chronic Sleep Restriction and Total Sleep Deprivation. *Sleep, 26(2),* 117-126.

Waterhouse, J., Atkinson, G., Edwards, B. & Reilly, T. (2007). The role of a short post-lunch nap in improving cognitive, motor, and sprint performance in participants with partial sleep deprivation. *Journal of Sports Science, 25(14),* 1557-1566.

Wired. (2019, Nov. 28). *Scientist Explains How Some People Need Only 4 Hours of Sleep* [Video]. YouTube. https://www.youtube.com/watch?v=eZnNgnPuQk0

Chapter 7 References

Atomic Heritage Foundation. (2014, Jun. 5). *Soviet Atomic Program – 1946*. Retrieved from https://www.atomicheritage.org/history/soviet-atomic-program-1946

Baseball Reference. (2020, May 17). *2019 Toronto Blue Jays Schedule*. Retrieved from https://www.baseball-reference.com/teams/TOR/2019-schedule-scores.shtml

Beaubien, J. (2012, Oct. 15). *Wiping Out Polio: How The U.S. Snuffed Out a Killer*. Retrieved from https://www.npr.org/sections/health-shots/2012/10/16/162670836/wiping-out-polio-how-the-u-s-snuffed-out-a-killer

Centers for Disease Control and Prevention. (2017, Nov. 3). *Our Progress Against Polio*. Retrieved from https://www.cdc.gov/polio/progress/index.htm

Cherry, K. (2019, Jun. 11). *How Many Neurons Are in the Brain?* Retrieved from https://www.verywellmind.com/how-many-neurons-are-in-the-brain-2794889

Chronaki, G. (2019, Oct. 23). *Curious Kids: how does our brain send signals to our body?* Retrieved from https://theconversation.com/curious-kids-how-does-our-brain-send-signals-to-our-body-124950

Davis, N. (2019, Oct. 23). *Blood pressure drugs work far better if taken at night, study shows*. Retrieved from https://www.theguardian.com/society/2019/oct/23/blood-pressure-drugs-work-far-better-if-taken-at-night-study-shows

Encyclopedia of World Biography. (2020, Apr. 27). *Jonas Salk Biography*. Retrieved from https://www.notablebiographies.com/Ro-Sc/Salk-Jonas.html

Facer-Childs, E. & Brandstaetter, R. (2015). The Impact of Circadian Phenotype and Time since Awakening on Diurnal Performance in Athletes. *Current Biology, 25,* 1-5.

Global Polio Eradication Initiative. (2010, Mar. 12). *GPEI Strategic Plan 2010-2012 Working Draft*. Retrieved from https://www.who.int/immunization/sage/GPEI_StrategicPlan_DRAFT.pdf?ua=1

Goel, N., Basner, M., Rao, H. & Dinges, D.F. (2013). Circadian Rhythms, Sleep Deprivation, and Human Performance. *Progress in Molecular Biology and Translational Science, 119,* 155-190.

Gur-Arie, R. (2014, June 21). *Cold Spring Harbor Laboratory (1890-)*. Retrieved from https://embryo.asu.edu/pages/cold-spring-harbor-laboratory-1890

Hoyle, N.P. et al (2017). Circadian actin dynamics drive rhythmic fibroblast mobilization during wound healing. *Science Translational Medicine, 9,* 415.

Hursh, S.R., Balkin, T.J., Miller, J.C. & Eddy, D.R. (2004). The Fatigue Avoidance Scheduling Tool: Modeling to Minimize the Effects of Fatigue on Cognitive Performance. *SAE International.* Retrieved from https://www.saftefast.com/downloads/SAE-Hursh-04DHM-14.pdf

Interchron. (2020, Apr. 28). *About Chronobiology.* Retrieved from https://interchron.org/about-chronobiology/

Janse van Rensburg, D.C. et al. (2020). How to manage travel fatigue and jet lag in athletes? A systematic review of interventions. *British Journal of Sports Medicine.* doi: 10.1136/bjsports-2019-101635.

Kleitman, N. & Jackson, D.P. (1950). Body temperature and performance under different routines. *Journal of Applied Physiology, 3(6),* 309-328.

Lee, A. & Galvez, J.C. (2012). Jet Lag in Athletes. *Sports Health, 4(3),* 211-216.

Marks, D.H. (2018, Oct.). *Jonas Salk, Polio Vaccine and Vaccinating Against Hate.* Retrieved from https://www.researchgate.net/publication/328231636_Jonas_Salk_Polio_Vaccine_and_Vaccinating_Against_Hate

Medical Xpress, Medical Research Council. (2017, Nov. 8). *Our body clocks cause wounds sustained at night to heal more slowly.* Retrieved from https://medicalxpress.com/news/2017-11-body-clocks-wounds-sustained-night.html

Monk, T.H. (2005). The Post-Lunch Dip in Performance. *Clinics in Sports Medicine, 24(2),* e15-23.

Museum of Health Care at Kingston. (2020, May 17). *Polio.* Retrieved from https://www.museumofhealthcare.ca/explore/exhibits/vaccinations/polio.html

National Institute of General Medical Services. (2017, Sept.). *Circadian Rhythms.* Retrieved from https://www.nigms.nih.gov/education/Documents/CircadianRhythms.pdf

National Institutes of Health. (2017, Oct. 2). *NIH Grantees Win 2017 Nobel Prize in Physiology or Medicine.* Retrieved from https://www.nih.gov/news-events/news-releases/nih-grantees-win-2017-nobel-prize-physiology-or-medicine

Nobel Media AB 2020. *The Nobel Prize in Physiology or Medicine 1954, John F. Enders.* Retrieved from https://www.nobelprize.org/prizes/medicine/1954/enders/facts/

Racaniello, V. (2007, Sept. 7). *Polio and Nobel Prizes.* Retrieved from https://www.virology.ws/2007/09/07/polio-and-nobel-prizes/

Reilly, T. (2009). How Can Travelling Athletes Deal with Jet-Lag? *Kinesiology, 41(2),* 128-135.

Roach, G.D. & Sargent, C. (2019). Interventions to Minimize Jet Lag After Westward and Eastward Flight. *Frontiers in Physiology, 10,* 927.

Salk Institute for Biological Studies. (2011, Oct. 3). *'Alarm clock' gene explains wake-up function of biological clock*. Retrieved from https://www.sciencedaily.com/releases/2011/09/110929161343.htm

Salk Institute for Biological Studies. (2013, May 20). *Timing of cancer radiation therapy may minimize hair loss, researchers say*. Retrieved from https://www.salk.edu/news-release/timing-of-cancer-radiation-therapy-may-minimize-hair-loss-researchers-say/

Salk Institute for Biological Studies. (2014, Aug. 13). *Single gene controls jet lag*. Retrieved from https://www.salk.edu/news-release/single-gene-controls-jet-lag/

Salk Institute for Biological Studies. (2018, Feb. 8). *Timing is everything, to our genes*. Retrieved from https://www.salk.edu/news-release/timing-everything-genes/

Salk Institute for Biological Studies. (2019, Oct. 15). *Novel technique helps explain why bright light keeps us awake*. Retrieved from https://www.salk.edu/news-release/novel-technique-helps-explain-why-bright-light-keeps-us-awake/

Salk Institute for Biological Studies. (2020, Apr. 27). *History of Salk – About Jonas Salk*. Retrieved from https://www.salk.edu/about/history-of-salk/jonas-salk/

Salk Institute for Biological Studies. (2020, Apr. 27). *History of Salk – Salk Institute*. Retrieved from https://www.salk.edu/about/history-of-salk/

Salk Institute for Biological Studies. (2020, May 17). *Scientist Directory – Faculty*. Retrieved from https://www.salk.edu/science/directory/faculty/?sort=lab

Smith, R.S., Efron, B., Mah, C.D. & Malhotra, A. (2013). The Impact of Circadian Misalignment on Athletic Performance in Professional Football Players. *Sleep, 36(12)*, 1999-2001.

Smith, R.S., Guilleminault, C. & Efron, B. (1997). Circadian Rhythms and Enhanced Athletic Performance in the National Football League. *Sleep, 20(5)*, 362-365.

Song, A., Severini, T. & Allada, R. (2017). How jet lag impairs Major League Baseball performance. *Proceedings of the National Academy of Sciences of the United States of America, 114(6)*, 1407-1412.

United Kingdom National Health Service. (2013, Sept. 2). *Researchers identify 'jet lag gene'*. Retrieved from https://www.nhs.uk/news/lifestyle-and-exercise/researchers-identify-jet-lag-gene/

University of Minnesota. (2020, May 17). *Halberg Chronobiology Center, Franz Halberg*. Retrieved from http://halbergchronobiologycenter.umn.edu/home/franz-halberg

REFERENCES

Winter, W.C., Hammond, W.R., Green, N.H., Zhang, Z. & Bliwise, D.L. (2009). Measuring Circadian Advantage in Major League Baseball: A 10-Year Retrospective Study. *International Journal of Sports Physiology and Performance, 4*, 394-401.

Witkowski, J.A. (2020, Apr. 28). *1960: Biological Clocks, Vol. XXV.* Retrieved from http://symposium.cshlp.org/site/misc/topic25.xhtml

Wood, R. (2008). *Beep Test Instructions.* Retrieved from https://www.topendsports.com/testing/tests/20mshuttle.htm

Wright, K.P. Jr., Hull, J.T. & Czeisler, C.A. (2002). Relationship between alertness, performance, and body temperature in humans. *American Journal of Physiology – Regulatory, Integrative and Comparative Physiology, 283(6),* R1370-R1377.

Chapter 8 References

American Academy of Pediatrics. (2011). *Mental Health Screening and Assessment Tools for Primary Care.* Retrieved from http://www.heardalliance.org/wp-content/uploads/2011/04/Mental-Health-Assessment.pdf

American College of Sports Medicine. (2013). Team Physician Consensus Statement: 2013 Update. *Medicine & Science in Sports & Exercise, 45(8),* 1618-1622.

Anytime Health, LLC. (2014, Mar. 10). *Strongmen of the 19th Century.* Retrieved from https://www.pumpone.com/blog/104

BBC Sport. (2018, Mar. 21). *Mental health action plan for elite athletes put in place by government.* Retrieved from https://www.bbc.com/sport/43483169

Berkowitz, S. (2018, Jul. 24). *Iowa strength coach Chris Doyle, already highest paid, gets a raise to $725,000.* Retrieved from https://www.usatoday.com/story/sports/ncaaf/bigten/2018/07/24/iowa-strength-coach-chris-doyle-gets-raise-725-000/829562002/

Bucher, A. (2020, May 22). *Amy Bucher, PhD: Bio and Experience.* Retrieved from https://www.amybucherphd.com/about/

Bucher, A. (2016, Jun. 8). *The Diminishing Returns of Education for Health Behavior Change.* Retrieved from https://www.amybucherphd.com/the-diminishing-returns-of-education-for-health-behavior-change/

Caia, J., Scott, T.J., Halson, S.L. & Kelly, V.G. (2018). The influence of sleep hygiene education on sleep in professional rugby league athletes. *Sleep Health, 4(4),* 364-368.

CBC Digital Archives. (1984, Feb. 25). *Fitness craze sweeps the nation.* Retrieved from https://www.cbc.ca/archives/entry/fitness-craze-sweeps-the-nation

Cleveland Cavaliers. (2018, Jan. 24). *Kevin Love Names 2018 All-Star Reserve.* Retrieved from https://www.nba.com/cavaliers/releases/love-all-star-reserve-180123

Colten, H.R. & Altevogt, B.M. (Ed.). (2006). *Sleep Disorders and Sleep Deprivation: An Unmet Public Health Problem.* Washington, D.C.: National Academies Press.

Columbia University, Department of Neurology. (2020, May 18). *Sleep Deprivation.* Retrieved from https://www.columbianeurology.org/neurology/staywell/document.php?id=42069

Communication with Vern Gambetta.

REFERENCES

Cooper Aerobics. (2020, May 24). *Kenneth H. Cooper, MD, MPH Full Bio.* Retrieved from https://cooperaerobics.com/About/Our-Leaders/Kenneth-H-Cooper,-MD,-MPH-Full-Bio.aspx

Cooper, K.H. (1968). *Aerobics.* New York: M. Evans and Company, Inc.

De Luca, M., Horovitz, R., Pitt, B. (Producers), & Miller, B. (Director). (2011). *Moneyball* [Motion Picture]. United States: Columbia Pictures.

Driller, M.W., Mah, C.D. & Halson, S.L. (2018). Development of the athlete sleep behavior questionnaire: A tool for identifying maladaptive sleep practices in elite athletes. *Sleep Science, 11(1),* 37-44. Retrieved from http://sleepscience.org.br/details/441/en-US

Emery, N. (2012, Jul. 31) *Our Unsustainable Culture of Medical Specialization.* Retrieved from https://www.theatlantic.com/health/archive/2012/07/our-unsustainable-culture-of-medical-specialization/260504/

Felber, S. (2014, Nov. 5). *Cultural differences impact on sleep patterns.* Retrieved from https://blog.withings.com/2014/11/05/cultural-differences-impact-on-sleep-patterns/

Feldman, D. (2017, Jan. 20). *Detailed summary of changes under the NBA's new Collective Bargaining Agreement.* Retrieved from https://nba.nbcsports.com/2017/01/20/detailed-summary-of-changes-under-the-nbas-new-collective-bargaining-agreement/

Foster, R. (2015, Nov. 9). *Why sleep could be the key to tackling mental illness.* Retrieved from https://theconversation.com/why-sleep-could-be-the-key-to-tackling-mental-illness-50102

Frances, A. (2017, Jan. 21). *We Have Too Many Specialists and Too Few General Practitioners.* Retrieved from https://www.huffpost.com/entry/we-have-too-many-speciali_b_9040898

Freeman, D., et al. (2017). The effects of improving sleep on mental health (OASIS): a randomised controlled trial with mediation analysis. *Lancet Psychiatry, 4,* 749-758.

Gambetta, V. (2020, May 23). *About Vern.* Retrieved from http://104.131.108.125/index.php?route=information/information&information_id=4

Goodreads, Inc. (2020, May 18). *Mark Twain Quotable Quote.* Retrieved from https://www.goodreads.com/quotes/2719201-i-have-never-taken-any-exercise-except-sleeping-and-resting

Hale, J. (2006, Apr. 4). *History of Strength and Conditioning Science.* Retrieved from https://ezinearticles.com/?History-of-Strength-and-Conditioning-Science&id=172473

Havis, R.J. (2018, Jan. 18). *The Surprising New Connection between Sleep and Mental Health*. Retrieved from https://www.talkspace.com/blog/the-surprising-new-connection-between-sleep-and-mental-health/

Jauhar, S. (2014, Aug. 19). *One Patient, Too Many Doctors: The Terrible Expense of Overspecialization*. Retrieved from https://time.com/3138561/specialist-doctors-high-cost/

Lukacs, J.D., (2010, Jun. 24). *Programs decades in the making*. Retrieved from https://www.espn.com/college-football/news/story?id=5312405

MacMullan, J. (2018, May 1). *The courageous fight to fix the NBA's mental health problem*. Retrieved from https://www.espn.com/nba/story/_/id/24382693/jackie-macmullan-kevin-love-paul-pierce-state-mental-health-nba

Mayo Clinic Staff. (2018, Nov. 20). *Napping: Do's and don'ts for healthy adults*. Retrieved from https://www.mayoclinic.org/healthy-lifestyle/adult-health/in-depth/napping/art-20048319

McCann, Z. (2012, June 1). *Sleep tracking brings new info to athletes*. Retrieved from https://www.espn.com/blog/playbook/tech/post/_/id/797/sleep-tracking-brings-new-info-to-athletes

Mental Health Association in Forsyth County. (2020, May 24). *What is Mental Illness?* Retrieved from https://www.triadmentalhealth.org/what-is-mental-illness/

MLB Collective Bargaining Agreement art. V (2017-2021).

Moyer, J. (2015, Jul. 1). *Bigger, stronger, faster … players have come a long way in short time*. Retrieved from https://www.espn.com/college-football/story/_/id/13175331/how-former-pole-vaulter-sparked-college-football-training-revolution

National Sleep Foundation. *Sleep Hygiene*. Retrieved from https://www.sleepfoundation.org/articles/sleep-hygiene

National Strength and Conditioning Association Board of Directors. (2017). NSCA Strength and Conditioning Professional Standards and Guidelines. *Strength and Conditioning Journal, 39(6)*, 1-23.

National Strength and Conditioning Association. (2020, May 18). *Who is the NSCA?* Retrieved from https://www.nsca.com/about-us/about-us/

NCAA Sport Science Institute. (2018, Jun. 1). *Anxiety Disorders*. Retrieved from https://www.ncaa.org/sites/default/files/2018SSI_Anxiety_Disorders_Fact%20Sheet_20180601.pdf

NCAA Sport Science Institute. (2020). *Inter-Association Consensus Document: Best Practices for Understanding and Supporting Student-Athlete Mental Wellness.* Retrieved from https://ncaaorg.s3.amazonaws.com/ssi/mental/SSI_MentalHealthBestPractices.pdf

NHL Collective Bargaining Agreement art. 16 (2012-2022).

NHL Collective Bargaining Agreement art. 16 (2005-2011).

Nova Southeastern University Athletics. *Hall of Fame: Larry Starr, Ed.D.* Retrieved from https://nsusharks.com/hof.aspx?hof=38&kiosk=true

Okamoto-Mizuno, K. & Mizuno, K. (2012). Effects of thermal environment on sleep and circadian rhythm. *Journal of Physiological Anthropology, 31,* 14

Pelissero, T. (2015, Oct. 22). *NFLPA files grievance over sleep monitoring devices being used by teams.* Retrieved from https://www.usatoday.com/story/sports/nfl/2015/10/22/nflpa-nfl-sleep-monitors/74402474/

Peterson, C. (2014, Sept. 23). *Strength and Conditioning: History and Overview of the Field.* (On file with author).

Professional Baseball Strength & Conditioning Coaches Society. (2015, Jan. 27). *History of Strength and Conditioning in Professional Baseball Part 1: The Beginnings (1976-1980).* Retrieved from http://baseballstrength.org/history-strength-and-conditioning-in-professional-baseball-part-1-the-beginnings-1976-1980/

Randle, A.K. (2011). *Weight Lifting & Weight Training.* North Carolina: Lulu Press, Inc.

Rogers, A.J., et al. (2017). Obstructive Sleep Apnea among Players in the National Football League: A Scoping Review. *Journal of Sleep Disorders and Therapy, 6(5),* 278.

Sleep Health Foundation. (2011, Oct. 14). *Common Causes of Inadequate Sleep.* Retrieved from https://www.sleephealthfoundation.org.au/common-causes-of-inadequate-sleep.html

SleepQuest, Inc. (2013). *Dr. Dement, The Father of Modern Sleep Science.* (On file with author).

Stepanski, E.J. (2002). The Effect of Sleep Fragmentation on Daytime Function. *SLEEP, 25(3),* 268-276.

Svoboda, J. (2019, Oct. 23). *The science of sleep helps Blue Jackets get ahead.* Retrieved from https://www.nhl.com/bluejackets/news/blue-jackets-undergo-teamwide-sleep-study/c-310365824

Thorpy, M.J. (2012). Classification of Sleep Disorders. *Neurotherapeutics, 9(4),* 687-701.

United States Government. (1950). *1950 Census of Population: Volume 1. Number of Inhabitants, Nebraska.* Retrieved from https://www2.census.gov/library/publications/decennial/1950/population-volume-1/vol-01-30.pdf

University of Eastern Finland. (2016, May 19). *Sleep disorders common in athletes, but easily fixable.* Retrieved from https://www.sciencedaily.com/releases/2016/05/160519082056.htm

University of Nebraska Athletics. (2020, May 24). *Boyd Epley.* Retrieved from http://www.nmnathletics.com/ViewArticle.dbml?&ATCLID=57&DB_OEM_ID=100

USA Strength and Conditioning Coaches Hall of Fame. *Boyd Epley.* Retrieved from https://www.usastrengthcoacheshf.com/member/boyd-epley

USA Today. (2020, May 22). *2019 NCAAF Strength Coaches Salaries.* Retrieved from https://sports.usatoday.com/ncaa/salaries/football/strength

Van Dongen, H.P.A., Maislin, G., Mullington, J.M. & Dinges, D.F. (2003). The Cumulative Cost of Additional Wakefulness: Dose-Response Effects on Neurobehavioral Functions and Sleep Physiology From Chronic Sleep Restriction and Total Sleep Deprivation. *Sleep, 26(2),* 117-126.

"Vern Gambetta." Retrieved on May 23, 2020, from https://www.linkedin.com/in/athdevcoachvgambetta

Wehrens, S.M.T. (2017). Meal Timing Regulates the Human Circadian System. *Current Biology, 27(12),* 1768-1775.e3.

Weingarten, J.A. & Collop, N.A. (2013). Air Travel: Effects of Sleep Deprivation and Jet Lag. *Chest, 144(4),* 1394-1401.

Wesensten, N.J., Balkin, T.J., & Belenky, G. (1999). Does sleep fragmentation impact recuperation? A review and reanalysis. *Journal of Sleep Research, 8,* 237-245.

Wolkenbrod, R. (2020, Jan. 28). *Amid Unknown Future, DeMar DeRozan Could Represent Spurs in All-Star Game.* Retrieved from https://www.forbes.com/sites/robwolkenbrod/2020/01/28/amid-unknown-future-demar-derozan-could-represent-spurs-in-all-star-game/#263501ff7b7a

Zen Arts. (2011, Oct. 13). *The Circus Strongman: Defying the Laws of Physics.* Retrieved from https://www.zenartsla.com/circus-strongman-defying-laws-physics/

Why We Wrote This Book References

Basketball Reference. *NBA MVP & ABA Most Valuable Player Award Winners.* Retrieved on June 10, 2020, from https://www.basketball-reference.com/awards/mvp.html

Communications with Bill Sweetenham.

Curtis, J. (2005, May 9). *Young Nash A Gem Waiting To Be Mined.* Retrieved from https://www.santaclarabroncos.com/sports/m-baskbl/2004-05/releases/050905aad.html

Duffy, K. (2014, Mar. 15). *Santa Clara University basketball coach on recruiting Canadian high school senior Steve Nash.* Retrieved from https://notableandquotable.blogspot.com/2014/03/santa-clara-university-basketball-coach.html

JockBio.com. *Steve Nash.* Retrieved on June 10, 2020, from https://www.jockbio.com/Bios/Nash/Nash_bio.html

NBA. *Steve Nash Stats.* Retrieved on June 10, 2020, from https://stats.nba.com/player/959/

INCONVENIENT SLEEP

Why We Wrote This Book

I'm writing a book. I've got the page numbers done.

Steven Wright

If only it was that easy...

Pat and Suzanne Byrne

The Journey

Every year in North America hundreds of thousands of high school basketball games are played by boys and girls. Most games are memorable only to the players and their families and friends. That was true for us as well. One game stood out and it greatly affected our lives.

The game was the 1991-92 senior boys AAA Provincial Basketball Championship final game in Vancouver, British Columbia. The

Victoria Blue Devils were playing the Pitt Meadows Marauders, one game for the Provincial Championship. By half-time the teams were close, they went to their dressing rooms to recoup. When the second half started the Blue Devils took over and eventually won. Two guards had battled each other all night long. It was fun to watch. However, their futures would diverge and later connect in a way no one could anticipate. The guard for the Marauders was Jay McBride and the guard for the Blue Devils was --- Steve Nash.

Steve Nash was an amazing high school basketball player but from a small town with no profile in America. He was not recruited by any NCAA team. His high school coach eventually sent letters to all the high-profile NCAA teams with a recommendation to recruit Steve. No positive response. No one was interested.

Eventually, Santa Clara University in California offered him a scholarship. Their coach was astounded to see Steve perform in person, "I was nervous as hell just hoping that no one else would see him. It didn't take a Nobel Prize winner to figure out this guy's pretty good. It was just a case of hoping that none of the big names came around." The team was excited.

Steve Nash went on to a great college career and was then selected 15th overall in the NBA draft by the Phoenix Suns. He played there for 2 seasons with Jason Kidd, an established NBA star, but did not get much playing time. He was then traded to the Dallas Mavericks in 1998 where he played for 6 seasons. Then, as a free agent he re-signed with the Phoenix Suns. There he played for eight seasons winning back-to-back league MVP awards. In 2012, Steve joined the Los Angeles Lakers and played there for two seasons before retiring as an NBA superstar. Not a bad career!!!

Jay McBride returned to his hometown of Pitt Meadows and followed his passion for basketball and the outdoors. He helped set up and volunteered for their "Little Dribblers" program teaching young children to play basketball. At the same time, he attended the British Columbia Institute of Technology where he studied forestry, his passion. When he graduated, Jay began his career as a forestry technician. Like many young workers Jay worked long hours and wanted to succeed, not paying much attention to when he slept. Within a few months Jay, after a long week, decided to drive off on a Friday night to see his girlfriend with his good friend, his black lab.

Tragically, Jay soon fell asleep and drove his car off an embankment. He died instantly. He was found alongside his good friend. His family, friends, the community and teammates were devastated. The Pitt Meadows City Council was so impressed with Jay's contributions to basketball in their community that they created and named an outdoor park in his name. The Jay McBride "Sports Court". At 22, the youngest person ever to be so honoured in that community. That facility is still actively used by young basketball players today.

Jay McBride was Pat's nephew and godson and Suzanne's cousin. His death changed their lives. At that time Pat was an occupational health and safety expert and the Canadian Director on the Board of the International Occupational Hygiene Association, an organization of 23 developed countries dedicated to occupational health and an NGO of the World Health Organization. Sleep and fatigue was not on anyone's radar. Not in industry and certainly not in sports.

Pat changed all that. His career began to focus on sleep and fatigue as a workplace issue. Eventually professional sports teams became interested in his work.

Ironically, 20 years later, he would go on to consult with the Brooklyn Nets and their coach, Jason Kidd. Both Suzanne and Pat also found themselves in the dressing room of Steve Nash's old team, the Dallas Mavericks, teaching Dirk Nowitzki and his teammates about sleep and fatigue. Dirk Nowitzki is a former colleague and long-time friend of Steve Nash.

The Coaches

Sports coaches can be inspirational. They have a strong desire to motivate their players to win and will do most anything to make that happen. Alain Vigneault is a successful NHL coach known for his sense of humour, his toughness, and his knowledge and experience. He was one of the first coaches, in any sport, to address sleep issues with his players. He also once said, "Don't tell my players they have a sleep problem unless you can fix it."

Alain was right. Telling athletes they have sleep problems without offering solutions can cause anxiety amongst athletes, often making the problem worse.

Bill Sweetenham was an Olympic swimming head coach 5 times; a Commonwealth games head coach 8 times and a World Champion head coach 9 times. He has coached 27 medalists, 9 world record holders and has been the Head Olympic National Swim Coach for Australia, Great Britain and Hong Kong and was awarded the Order of Australia. He continues to coach successful swim teams globally.

Bill Sweetenham relayed a story that illustrates the ingenuity of coaches. "Once I was on a flight from Beijing to Honk Kong and was coughing from all the smokers around me. It was terrible,

I could hardly breathe. I asked the flight attendant if I could be in a non-smoking seat, I couldn't take it anymore. She agreed and later returned with a sign reading "no smoking" and placed it on my seat!! I had the only non-smoking seat in the smoking section. It wasn't helpful!"

Bill thought about that experience and like many successful coaches found a way to turn adversity into an advantage. "There was no escaping the smoke." He knew intuitively that cigarette smoke was harmful to him and his players. "I didn't have any science to know how bad it was, at that time. I just knew we would be better off not breathing it in." Bill had a solution.

"When I booked the flights for our swim team to Vancouver from Sydney and back (a 14-hour one-way flight) to the 1994 Commonwealth Games I booked my entire swim team in the smoking section."

They took up the entire smoking section preventing anyone from smoking on the plane. Advantage Australia. By 1998 smoking was banned on all international flights. Advantage lost.

"I also knew that sleep was important for our athletes. Again, I didn't know exactly how it would affect their performance, but I knew that more sleep should result in better performance." He understood that jet lag would be a problem considering the long flight from Sydney and the 17-hour time change.

He had the team arrive in Canada a few days ahead to try to get over their jet lag. Not scientific, just intuitive. Not an overly sophisticated approach but likely the best approach given the technology and science of the day. Improving his players' sleep by reducing the effects of jet lag was one thing, helping to reduce the amount of sleep of their opponents was another.

"I made sure that all the other swim teams had plenty of access to free coffee and chocolate 24/7 but wouldn't let my team touch them." He was also known to provide free movie tickets to the midnight showings of popular movies … to other teams, so they would stay up late. A nice gesture; a competitive coach.

Progressive coaches are often open to trying anything that will give their team an advantage. Sleep is no exception. However, trainers are often the ones who have to implement the coach's great ideas. Trainers have said to us, "Please don't talk to our coaches, they'll make us do all this sleep stuff and we don't have time for it."

We wrote this book for the coaches, the athletes, the trainers, the officials (and for everyone who sleeps). We have had the great privilege of working in professional sports and have learned a lot. Much of what we've learned could not be published as we treasure the privacy of teams and athletes as much as they do. We did, however, do our best to share our experiences and insights into the importance of sleep for athletes and teams and to explain what can realistically be accomplished with regards to sleep.

Lightning Source UK Ltd.
Milton Keynes UK
UKHW010649151220
375173UK00001B/320